THE DAY NIAGARA FALLS RAN DRY!

THE DAY
NIAGARA FALLS
RAN DRY!

CANADIAN WEATHER FACTS
AND TRIVIA

D A V I D   P H I L L I P S

KEY PORTER BOOKS

Canadian
Geographic

Canadian Cataloguing in Publication Data

Phillips, D.W.
    The day Niagara Falls ran dry!: Canadian weather facts and trivia

Includes index.
ISBN 1-55013-491-4

1. Canada – Climate. I. Title.

QC985.P55 1993   551.6'0971   C93-094224-8

The publisher gratefully acknowledges the assistance of the Canada Council and the Government of Ontario.

Key Porter Books Limited
70 The Esplanade
Toronto, Ontario
Canada M5E 1R2

Design: Annabelle Stanley
Illustrations: Jack McMaster
Typesetting: MacTrix DTP
Printed and bound in Canada
    94 95 96 97 6 5 4 3 2

CONTENTS

WEATHERWISE

BELIEVE IT, WEATHER FORECASTING IS GETTING BETTER

BEING A WEATHER FORECASTER IN CANADA IS NOT EASY. There are no large deserts or tropical climes where the weather is the same day after day. And the adage, if you don't like the weather wait around for a few hours, is true almost everywhere. Moreover, the public's expectation for accurate weather forecasts has increased dramatically. At one time, Canadians were pleased with an occasional correct forecast. Today we expect perfection — not just whether it will rain or snow, which can be difficult enough to predict, but exactly when, precisely where and how much.

People tend to notice when forecasts are wrong, but overlook the many times they are correct. This isn't surprising, since it is the incorrect ones that cause the most inconvenience. Nevertheless, holding forecasters responsible for whatever happens in the skies, as some people do, is rather unfair. Fortunately, for the egos of forecasters, six out of ten Canadians feel forecasts are correct at least 70 percent of the time.

❄ As recently as the 1960s, British law decreed that if you were guilty of trying to predict the weather, you could be burned at the stake as a heretic.

Just the same, the forecaster is constantly being humbled by the "busts," when the weather is completely unlike the prediction. Canadians know them only too well — a thaw that never comes; 20 centimetres of "light flurries"; a sunny weekend that ends up wet and cloudy; or a springtime day that resembles midwinter.

The most infamous forecast in Canadian history was likely the prediction by the Halifax weather office for "a few flurries" across Nova Scotia on February 2, 1960. Within 24 hours, a record snowfall of 75 centimetres crippled Halifax, while 96 centimetres fell in the surrounding area. The story was big enough that one of the Halifax meteorologists was subsequently featured on CBC's "Front Page Challenge." When asked, "What are you doing in Toronto?" he replied, "Taking a refresher course in weather forecasting" — and gave the story away.

❄ It costs each Canadian about 2 cents per day for Environment Canada to observe the weather, issue daily forecasts and disseminate severe weather warnings.

Every meteorologist learns from his or her gaffes and presses on, knowing that in spite of occasional howls of indignation and some good-natured ribbing, 89 percent of Canadians start their days tuning in to the weather forecast.

New techniques and technology have transformed weather forecasting over the past 50 years, but the basic steps — collecting data, making the prediction, and transmitting forecasts and warnings — have not changed much in that time. Each day, nearly 300 manned or automatic monitoring stations across Canada take hourly pressure, wind, visibility, temperature and precipitation recordings. Thirty-seven additional stations simultaneously sample the upper atmosphere using instrument-laden balloons. These data and those from a worldwide network of 9,000 surface and 1,000 upper-atmosphere stations pour into the computers at the Canadian Meteorological Centre (CMC) in Montreal, sometimes in less than an hour after the data were recorded.

CMC is the nerve centre for forecast operations in Canada. Its modern, high-speed computer immediately

❄ The NEDC SX/3-44 computer located at the Canadian Meteorological Centre in Montreal is capable of doing 22 billion operations per second. It is 300,000 times faster than the first computer Canada used for forecasts in 1962.

maps extant weather systems and starts the intricate process of projecting future weather patterns, using complex equations. Within three hours of the original observations, weather charts forecasting up to five days in advance are transmitted to nine regional weather centres across the country.

Experienced regional forecasters use the computer analysis, as well as satellite photographs, radar images and other information, to produce detailed regional forecasts and weather warnings. Charts and written forecasts are sent to Environment Canada weather offices and are simultaneously distributed to the media and the public via broadcast news services, Weatheradio, and The Weather Network. Scarcely anyone in Canada does not have access to up-to-date weather information in one form or another.

Each year Environment Canada issues a staggering 800,000 forecasts for 436 different areas. Local forecasts for up to a 36- or 48-hour period are issued four times daily and updated as often as necessary. Extended forecasts — looking ahead three to five days — are issued twice daily. Warnings of hazardous weather, such as snowstorms, freezing rain, frost, hail, extreme rain and floods, tornadoes and wind storms, are issued as warranted.

❄ Each year Environment Canada issues 800,000 forecasts and 4,500 weather warnings.

Evaluating forecast accuracy would seem to be an easy task. After all, did it or did it not rain? Was it sunny? Did the day's high reach the low 20s? In actual fact, determining a final "grade" is not so simple. One of the major difficulties is establishing when a forecast is correct. For example, if a forecast predicts a low of

12°C and the temperature falls to 9°C, only three degrees off, is that forecast correct? A forecast of heavy snow for Toronto that misses the city by only 20 kilometres might be considered a reasonably good forecast by a meteorologist, but two million people who did not see any snow will think it was dead wrong! Should a forecast that correctly predicts snow and temperature but misses the cloud cover or wind speed be graded excellent, fair or failure? Verification is complicated by the many kinds of forecasts, the weather situation, the number of variables (temperature, precipitation, sky conditions, etc.), and the size of the forecast area (the smaller the area, the more difficult it is to score well).

The usefulness of the forecast to the user is also worth considering. A three-degree error in the night's minimum temperature is not as much a problem at 20°C as it would be near the freezing mark.

Ideally, procedures for verifying the accuracy of forecasts should be consistent over a long period of time in order to assess the impact of technological advances or improvements in analytical methods. Environment Canada tallies temperature scores by how much the forecast maximum and minimum differ from the actual temperature. For precipitation probability, forecasts are generally converted to categorical rain/no rain prospects. Anything below 50 percent is considered a forecast of no rain and would score perfect marks if no rain occurred in the forecast area for the period in question.

> ❄ The federal government began providing weather services in Canada in 1871, when Parliament allocated $5,000 for the communication of meteorological observations. Initially, the main focus was upon transportation — at first maritime, later aviation. Today, weather services are provided to many areas in industry, agriculture, forestry, tourism and the environment. Weather services today cost more than $200 million annually.

The public's confidence in the accuracy and usefulness of forecasts is not misplaced. Statistics from across Canada in 1990 for the 5 a.m. forecast show Environment Canada's temperature predictions for afternoon highs were within five degrees of the actual temperature 95 percent of the time; for nighttime lows, 92 percent of the time; and for the next day's high, 89 percent of the time. At a finer level of accuracy — within three degrees — the accuracy of forecasts was 82 percent, 75 percent and 71 percent, respectively. Precipitation forecasts were correct 77 percent of the time for same-day forecasts and 73 percent for the next day. In each case, there has been a three- to four-percent improvement in accuracy over a 10 year period.

❄ In 1945, John von Neumann, a Hungarian-American mathematician, built an electronic computer known as MANIAC. It was the first machine to be used for weather forecasting.

Slowly, but surely, weather forecasting is getting better. Forecast quality has improved about one percent a year, thanks to more sophisticated computers, more realistic physical or numerical models, and more reliable data, especially from weather satellites and Doppler radar, which measures wind speed as well as the amount and rate of precipitation. Seventy-two-hour forecasts are now as accurate as 36-hour forecasts were in 1957. We have gained a day and a half. Overall, a figure of 80 percent or more is a fair degree of accuracy for the forecast of the next day's weather. Beyond two days, however, accuracy decreases rapidly. Three-day forecasts are accurate 70 percent of the time; four-day forecasts 62 percent; and five-day forecasts only 53 percent.

Forecast accuracy varies greatly, depending on the location, the weather variables, the season, and the time period for which the prediction is made. Precipitation is harder to predict than temperature, especially the amount and timing. Also, the more extreme the event, the more difficult it is to forecast. Winter storms are generally easier to predict than summer storms, because they are larger and more uniform. They pose their own challenge, though. Will they bring rain, snow, freezing rain or a mixture of all three?

Weather forecasts still have plenty of room for improvement. Monitoring stations are too widely spaced. Imprecise predictive models are based on too many assumptions and neglect the effects of local physical features, such as hills, escarpments, lakes and rivers. Of course, better models require bigger and faster computers. But even if we multiplied the number of observation stations and operated super-speed computers, missing data or slight computational error would still magnify errors. When this happens, the location of fronts can be offset by more than 100 kilometres or ignored altogether. Misplaced fronts or errors of 1° or 2°C in temperature can make all the difference between calling for rain, snow, freezing rain, a mixture of precipitation or none at all.

Forecasting is simply one of the toughest challenges in the scientific world. Even perfect knowledge of the position and weather associated with large-scale highs and lows will not guarantee that meteorologists will be able to detect small-scale disturbances like squalls, thunderstorms and tornadoes. In general, the larger the storm and the longer its life cycle, the more precise one can be about

❄ Environment Canada alerts Canadians to severe summer storms by issuing weather watches and warnings. If a *watch* is issued in your area, maintain your normal routine, but keep an eye skyward for threatening weather, and listen to the radio or watch television for further weather information. When severe local storms are impending, or have actually been sighted or detected by radar, then *warnings* are issued. These may be either severe thunderstorm warnings or tornado warnings. Warnings mean you should be on the alert.

7

❄ A 1991 national survey on Canadian cable services found that The Weather Network had a 79 percent awareness rating among Canadians, higher than any other service including The Sports Network at 70 percent and MuchMusic at 61 percent.

where and when the storm will occur. Small-scale and short-term events such as thunderstorms, which can develop and dissipate within 20 minutes, are particularly tricky. Predicting the first thunderstorm of a July afternoon is somewhat like putting a pot of water on the stove to boil and trying to predict when and where the first bubble is going to occur. The forecaster can reliably predict that a severe thunderstorm or shower may occur during a summer afternoon, but there is no way of predicting exactly where and when the disturbance will actually appear until one sees the storm or detects it on radar.

When it comes to forecasting next month's weather or next season's the consensus is that you could do almost as well by flipping a coin. At best, monthly forecasts are estimates of whether the temperature and precipitation will be above, below or nearly normal for a region. Environment Canada only issues monthly temperature forecasts, having decided that a forecast of next month's precipitation is no better than a forecast that simply stays with the prevailing weather. In October 1992, Environment Canada inaugurated an air-temperature outlook for the forthcoming winter season. A team of climatologists applied some of the analytical procedures used for the 30-day forecasts, and followed the same reporting procedures: that is, temperatures are expressed as departures above or below the long-term normal or average.

With such innovations, the future of weather forecasting looks bright. Progress in the basic steps of forecasting — data acquisition, forecast analysis and information dissemination — will ensure continued improvement in forecast accuracy. By the end of the decade, seven-day forecasts should be as accurate as the five-day outlook is now. Greater attention to shorter, smaller-scale and more severe systems will result in more reliable and site-specific warnings of severe storms, as much as 30 minutes ahead of their occurrence, instead of the present five minutes.

But even with improvements on the horizon, predicting the nature of tomorrow's skies will never be easy in Canada. The weather will always hold surprises. The public will still criticize missed forecasts. And forecasters will always make the odd miscalculation — and continue to attend refresher school.

IT'S NOT THE COLD, IT'S THE WIND

A LERT ON THE NORTHERN TIP OF ELLESMERE ISLAND may be the coldest place in Canada, but the corner of Portage and Main in Winnipeg *feels* the coldest. Winnipeggers waiting for a bus on a blustery winter day outside the James Richardson Building may think the temperature is less cold in a doorway or in a bus shelter, but all they are really doing is escaping the chilling effect of the wind.

Wind chill is the popular name used to describe what cold weather feels like at various combinations of low temperature and high wind. The loss of body heat increases with a rise in wind speed, so that at the same temperature, a person will feel colder when the wind is blowing than when it is not. The wind lowers a person's temperature by evaporating moisture on

> ❄ It feels just as cold at –1°C with a 60 kilometre an hour wind speed as it does at –18°C with an 8 kilometre per hour wind.

9

and blowing heat away from the skin. Inanimate objects that have no heat to lose — a mailbox or a metal fence, for instance — are not affected by wind at all.

The more pronounced the air movement — wind or moving air produced by walking, skiing, or riding on a snowmobile or in a convertible — and the greater the temperature difference between the surface of the object and the air, the greater the heat loss. Wind cooling is what happens when we blow on a mug of steaming hot chocolate to cool it to room temperature. But you can't make it cooler than room-temperature, no matter how hard you blow. Similarly, no matter how strong the wind blows, it cannot lower the temperature below that of the surrounding air.

> ❄ Environment Canada forecasts include wind chill when values are expected to exceed 1,600 watts per square metre (−25°C); warnings are issued when values reach 2,300 watts per square metre (−50°C), the point at which exposed flesh freezes in less than one minute.

The American polar explorer and geographer, Paul Siple, first used the term *wind chill* in 1939. During the second expedition of Admiral Richard Byrd, Siple and his partner, Charles Passel, conducted experiments at Little America Antarctica, on the time required to freeze water in plastic vials exposed outside in wind. They developed a formula for relating heat loss to wind speed and air temperature, expressed in units of atmospheric cooling; that is, watts per square metre. Later, the formula was modified to allow computation of a wind chill equivalent temperature.

Of course, there is a considerable difference between water-filled plastic tubes and a person properly clothed for the weather. The Siple–Passel approach is only an estimate of the discomfort felt by humans under various temperature and wind conditions. It does not take into account many other factors important for determining a person's sensitivity to cold — whether the person is running, walking or sitting; whether the sun is shining; what the humidity is; the person's age and physical condition; and the amount and insulation quality of garments worn. All of these factors can affect the rate of cooling of the human body. Nevertheless, in spite of its shortcomings and the many efforts to develop a more comprehensive measure of cooling discomfort, Siple and Passel's simple formula is widely used.

Wind chill graphs, tables in metric and imperial units, and computer programs abound. The public and the military find wind chill estimates helpful in deciding how much clothing is required to protect against the cold and wind. It is also a valuable indicator of the likelihood of frostbite and excessive loss of body heat, or hypothermia. For these reasons, Environment Canada issues warnings for severe wind chill episodes.

Two ways of expressing the wind chill are the heat loss in watts per square metre and the equivalent air temperature in degrees Celsius. On page 12 are examples of wind chill values and their effects.

The highest wind chill values in Canada are found in January over the Barrens northwest of Hudson Bay. Baker Lake, Northwest Territories, has the highest wind chill in Canada. Farther north over the arctic islands, wind speeds are less than those in the southern Arctic,

❄ • Pets left outside feel the wind chill.
• Block heaters facing the wind are less effective in keeping car engines warm than those facing away from the wind.
• Home fuel consumption goes up on cold, windy days.
• Wind chill values tend to be higher over exposed terrain and on street corners than in forest clearings and streets sheltered by tall buildings.
• The dangers of overexposure to severe cold are brought on faster with strong winds; a prolonged windy, cold period may lead to frostbite, exposure and hypothermia.
• Wet clothing or footgear has a much-reduced insulating value and will result in a body heat loss nearly equal to that of exposed skin.

EXAMPLES OF WIND CHILL EFFECTS

Wind Chill Factor (Watts per square metre)	Equivalent Temperature (°C)	Effects
700	−3	Conditions considered comfortable when dressed for skiing.
1,200	−11	Conditions no longer pleasant for outdoor activities on overcast days.
1,400	−18	Conditions no longer pleasant for outdoor activities on sunny days.
1,600	−25	Freezing of exposed skin begins for most people depending on the degree of activity and the amount of sunshine.
2,300	−50	Conditions for outdoor travel, such as walking, become dangerous. Exposed areas freeze in less than one minute for the average person.
2,700	−66	Exposed flesh freezes within half a minute on average.

CALCULATING WIND CHILL

You can calculate the wind chill equivalent temperature in degrees Celsius (°C) or the wind chill factor in watts per square metre for your own values of air temperature (°C) and wind speed in kilometres per hour, by using the following equations:

(1) wind chill equivalent temperature

$$WET = 33 - ((12.1 + 6.12 \sqrt{W} - 0.32 * W) (33 - T) / 27.8)$$

(2) wind chill factor

$$WCF = (12.1 + 6.12 \sqrt{W} - 0.32 * W) (33 - T)$$

WET	=	wind chill equivalent temperature (°C)
T	=	ambient air temperature in °C
W	=	wind speed in kilometres per hour
WCF	=	wind chill factor (watts per square metre)

This gives meaningful values of WET and WCF for any air temperature lower than 5°C, and for any wind speed between 8 and 80 kilometres per hour.

WIND CHILL TABLES

WIND CHILL (WATTS PER SQUARE METRE)

Temperature °C

Wind (km/h)	0	–5	–10	–15	–20	–25	–30	–35
10	933	1,075	1,216	1,358	1,499	1,641	1,782	2,009
20	1,092	1,257	1,423	1,588	1,753	1,919	2,084	2,248
30	1,189	1,369	1,549	1,729	1,909	2,089	2,269	2,449
40	1,253	1,443	1,633	1,823	2,013	2,202	2,393	2,583
50	1,298	1,494	1,691	1,887	2,084	2,280	2,477	2,673
60	1,327	1,529	1,730	1,931	2,132	2,334	2,535	2,736

WIND CHILL TEMPERATURE (°C)

Temperature °C

Wind (km/h)	0	–5	–10	–15	–20	–25	–30	–35
10	–2	–7	–12	–17	–22	–27	–32	–38
20	–7	–13	–19	–25	–31	–37	–43	–50
30	–11	–17	–24	–31	–37	–44	–50	–57
40	–13	–20	–27	–34	–41	–48	–55	–62
50	–15	–22	–29	–36	–44	–51	–58	–66
60	–16	–23	–31	–38	–45	–53	–60	–68

and consequently the wind chill is also lower. Some southern cities also experience high wind chills. Winnipeg has wind chills comparable to those in the High Arctic and Montreal's are not unlike those in the relatively calm Yukon. In January the percentage of time that the wind chill exceeds –20°C (1,400 watts per square metre), or the shivering point, is 83 percent at Winnipeg,

COLDEST WIND CHILL DAYS ACROSS CANADA

Province/ Territory	Wind Chill (°C)/W/sqm	Location	Date	Temp- erature	Wind (km/h)
Northwest Territories	–92/3,357	Pelly Bay	13/01/75	–51	56
Yukon	–83/3,152	Komakuk Beach	12/02/75	–50	40
British Columbia	–69/2,749	Old Glory Mtn.	15/12/64	–36	50
Alberta	–68/2,740	Red Deer	15/12/64	–35	61
Saskatchewan	–70/2,757	Swift Current	15/12/64	–34	89
Manitoba	–76/2,938	Churchill	18/01/75	–41	56
Ontario	–70/2,753	Thunder Bay	10/01/82	–36	54
Quebec	–77/3,001	Nitchequon	20/01/75	–42	56
New Brunswick	–61/2,547	Charlo	18/01/82	–31	54
Nova Scotia	–53/2,309	Sydney	18/01/82	–25	59
Prince Edward Island	–57/2,450	Charlottetown	18/01/82	–32	37
Newfoundland/ Labrador	–71/2,814	Wabush Lake	20/01/75	–41	40

62 percent at Edmonton, 42 percent at Ottawa, 17 percent at Halifax and under one percent at Vancouver and Victoria.

The coldest wind chill, since Canadian recordings were begun in 1953, occurred at Pelly Bay, Northwest Territories, on January 13, 1975, when the equivalent wind chill temperature was –92°C and the heat loss was 3,357. At the time, the air temperature was –51°C and the winds were 56 kilometres per hour. Edmonton's worst episode was on December 15, 1964, with a numbing wind chill reading of –67°C or 2,732. Winnipeg's longest skin-freezing wind chill spell lasted 170 consecutive hours beginning on January 24, 1966; Saskatoon, however had one that lasted 215 hours commencing on December 28, 1978.

A windy winter's day before World War II on Ouellette Avenue in Windsor, Ontario. ONTARIO ARCHIVES

THE GREATEST STORMS ON EARTH

I N 1989, HURRICANE GILBERT CAPTURED NEWSPAPER headlines for about a week in September as it rampaged through Mexico and the countries of the Caribbean. It was a world record breaker, the most powerful hurricane yet recorded in the Western Hemisphere, and one of the wettest systems ever seen in modern times. Destruction from Gilbert and local storms spawned from it spread from Venezuela to Texas. Jamaica was the hardest hit. Some 50,000 people needed shelter for weeks to months

Thirty-seven people died on this riverside street in Toronto during Hurricane Hazel. CANAPRESS

after the storm, because nearly three-quarters of the country's buildings were destroyed. Damage costs reached $2 billion and the entire Jamaican power grid had to be reconstructed. Remarkably, Gilbert claimed only 318 lives, far fewer than some of the infamous storm killers of this century; at least six of them killed over 1,000 people each, and two, Galveston in 1900 and Flora in 1963, killed 6,000 each.

North Americans call them hurricanes. In China and Japan they are known as typhoons; in countries around the Indian Ocean, cyclones. To Filipinos and other southeast Asians, they are baguios. No matter what they are called, these enormous spiralling weather systems are the greatest storms on earth. The United Nation's World Meteorological Organization estimates that in an average year, 80 of them kill up to 15,000 people and cause several billion dollars worth of property damage.

Most North American hurricanes develop over the Atlantic within 20 degrees of the equator. Each year hundreds of weather disturbances, or cyclonic storms, form in the easterly trade winds over the tropical ocean, but fewer than 10 become full-fledged hurricanes.

Although not fully understood, many factors are involved in the creation of these mammoth storms. In most cases, intense sunlight heats the ocean, which in turn warms the overriding air by convection. The heated air rises, carrying away evaporated water charged with energy, and producing an area of low pressure. The process quickens as more and more air and water spiral upwards. The air cools, condenses and releases the sun's energy stored in the evaporated water. So awesome is the rate of heat-energy release inside a mature hurricane, it has been calculated that if it could be transformed into electricity, it would amount to 10 trillion kilowatts of power, or 8,000 times the amount produced in Canada on any given day, enough to supply the entire country for 30 years.

It takes a complex series of chain reactions and self-feeding processes to create a hurricane. While the storm intensifies, the pressure in its central column is further lowered, creating a partial vacuum. More ocean air is sucked in and sent higher into the atmosphere as the whirlpool-like vortex spins faster. Within a few days, the minor disturbance that

❋ Several derivations of the word *hurricane* exist. One version originates with the natives of the West Indies, based on the word, *huracan,* referring to a "great wind" or evil spirit. Another possibility is from the Guatemalan Indian god for stormy weather, *Hunraken.*

❋ Ninety percent of all hurricane fatalities occur in the storm surge — an abnormal rise of the sea level created by low pressure and high tide.

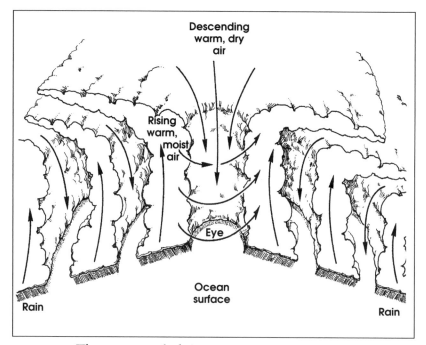

The structure of a hurricane.

began innocuously on a calm, humid day is transformed
into an enormous, whirling weather machine.

An important feature of the hurricane is the inward
spiralling motion initiated by the earth's rotation — a
counterclockwise motion in the Northern Hemisphere
and a clockwise motion in the Southern Hemisphere.
Seen from above, the hurricane appears as a spiralling
mass of cloud converging into a small area free of cloud.
Outside this central column, the strongest winds swirl
and roar at more than 180 kilometres per hour accompanied by a constant deluge. Paradoxically, at the heart of
the storm exists a world of calm and sunshine in what is
known as the "eye." Many people have been lured from
shelter when the eye passed overhead, only to be caught

by the violent winds from the opposite side of the hurricane.

The main system of cloud, rain and wind extends about 60 to 90 kilometres out from the centre of the eye. Farther out, stretching over tens of thousands of square kilometres in spiral bands, conditions are less extreme, but winds can still be violent and the rain heavy. At some point, the young hurricane starts to move slowly, usually advancing at a speed of 15 to 25 kilometres per hour. While moving out of the tropics, it gradually accelerates, often wreaking havoc along the way. But once the storm moves out of the tropical zone and into cooler northern latitudes, it quickly dies out — either starved of heat energy and moisture when it encounters cold seas or dragged apart by ground friction when it meets land. The farther north from the equator the storm moves, the more likely it is to get caught in the prevailing westerlies. Eventually, it recurves to the north and northeast. That is the main reason hurricanes seldom strike Canada with full force.

The average lifetime of a hurricane is nine days. Some, however, may last only a few hours, while others continue for a whole month. The North Atlantic hurricane season extends from June through November, although 84 percent of the storms occur between August and October. They reach their greatest fury and frequency in September when the surface ocean temperature is at a peak of about 27°C.

❄ Names of infamous hurricanes are retired from further use. Among the names retired: Agnes, 1972; Alicia, 1983; Allen, 1980; Andrew, 1992; Bob, 1991; Camille, 1969; David, 1979; Elena, 1985; Frederick, 1979; Gilbert, 1988; Gloria, 1985; Hazel, 1954; Hugo, 1989; Joan, 1988.

❄ The most powerful tornadoes may have winds of 500 kilometres per hour or more. The most powerful hurricanes may have sustained surface wind speeds of 250 kilometres per hour with gusts as high as 320.

❋ The first "male" hurricane in the Atlantic was actually a wimp. In 1979, Hurricane Bob barely made it over the 120-kilometre-per-hour speed limit to qualify as a hurricane. In 1991, however, Bob was deadly and the name was retired.

The most destructive elements of a hurricane are often the huge waves, storm tides and flooding it generates. For a day ahead of the storm, the ocean builds into a monstrous wall of water that eventually comes crashing ashore. Sea levels are pushed up as much as five metres higher than normal tides, flooding low-lying coastal areas. Hurricane winds have produced waves as tall as 10-storey buildings; a United States Navy ship's commander reported encountering a 34-metre-high wave in 1933. While the direct effects of a hurricane can be devastating, the tornadoes they frequently spawn, which have even higher wind speeds, can also take a heavy toll.

Of the ten tropical cyclones that develop each year in the North Atlantic, only six will become hurricanes, and only one or two will enter cool Canadian waters. By then, after travelling 15,000 kilometres, most have lost much of their sting. Generally, the only regions affected in this country range from the Atlantic provinces through Quebec to Ontario east of Lake Superior.

❋ *Cyclone* was the name given to intense circular storms by Captain H. Piddington in 1848. Today, *cyclone* refers to the family of storms that includes hurricanes, typhoons, tornadoes and depressions.

Typhoons seldom stray into our Pacific waters, which are too cold to sustain hurricane intensities. Typhoon Freda, or at least its remnants, struck the Pacific northwest on October 12, 1962. In Victoria, where winds reached sustained speeds of 74 kilometres per hour with gusts to 145, there were seven storm-related deaths and damage exceeded $10 million.

Hurricane Hazel is the most-remembered

storm in Canadian history, striking south-ern Ontario on October 15, 1954. An estimated 300 million tonnes of rain fell on Toronto. In its wake, the storm left a nightmare of destruction in and around the city — lost streets, washed-out bridges and untold personal tragedy. Losses included 80 dead and $100 million damage.

Other less famous but equally or more destructive hurricanes have reached Canada. Hurricane Beth on August 16, 1971, produced more rain than Hazel, dumping 296 millimetres on Nova Scotia. An unnamed hurricane struck southwestern Ontario on September 25, 1941; in London, 130-kilometre-per-hour winds were recorded, stronger than those that accompanied Hazel. The dead-liest hurricanes to strike Canada were the unnamed storms that hit the Maritimes on August 25, 1873, sinking 1,200 vessels, and the "Independence Hurricane" that struck Newfoundland on September 9, 1775, drown-ing several thousand British seamen.

Originally, hurricanes were sometimes named for the saint's day on which they occurred or for large ships sunk by the storm. At the turn of the century, Australian meteorologist Clement Wragge assigned female names to tropical storms, and male names, especially politi-cians', to other storms. However, for most of the first half of this century, hurricanes went unnamed.

The practice was revived during

> ❄ The most deadly hurricane (typhoon, cyclone) in history was in the Bay of Bengal in 1737 when 300,000 persons were drowned. In 1991, more than 125,000 people were killed in a cyclone in Bangladesh. The disaster left 10 million people homeless.

> ❄ Only about seven percent of the Atlantic hurri-canes have any noticeable effect on the weather in southern Ontario and only about two percent have high winds and exces-sive rainfall.

World War II when American armed services meteorologists attached the names of their wives or girlfriends to hurricanes, especially when two or more storms appeared on the weather map at the same time. A system of latitude-longitude identification was also used but was considered too cumbersome for practical use, particularly when more than one hurricane was present over the same ocean. During the 1940s, the media got into the hurricane name game as well, calling the first storm in 1949 Hurricane Harry (Truman) and a subsequent, more violent storm Hurricane Bess, after the president's wife. Other identification systems survived a year or so, for example naming hurricanes by letters of

Waiting to be rescued after Hurricane Hazel. CANAPRESS

the alphabet, as in radio code words Able, Baker, Charlie, and so forth. One system even used a new, international phonetic alphabet.

In 1953, American military communicators suggested using female names in alphabetical order. The practice was adopted by the United States Weather Service, despite thousands of letters of complaint, especially after Hurricane Hazel struck so savagely. Weather sexism continued for 24 years until 1978. Although the weather service contended that mail favouring the feminine name system far exceeded that against it, in 1979 the World Meteorological Organization initiated the use of a preselected list of male and female names organized alphabetically. That practice is still in force today. Short, distinctive English, French and Hispanic names are used and repeated every six years; names associated with infamy — Hazel, Agnes, Gilbert, Hugo — are not used again. The letters Q, U, X, Y and Z are not used because of the scarcity of names beginning with those letters. Separate lists are prepared for both the eastern Pacific and northern Atlantic tropical storms.

❄ Tropical systems are classed into several categories depending on maximum strength, usually measured by maximum sustained wind speed. A *tropical disturbance* is simply a moving area of thunderstorms in the tropics that maintains its identity for 24 hours or more. A *tropical depression* is a cyclonic system originating over the tropics that has a highest sustained wind speed of up to 61 km/h. A *tropical storm* has a highest sustained wind speed between 62 and 117 km/h. A *hurricane* has wind speeds of 118 km/h or more.

Here are some of the beauties and beasts you may see or hear about on the northern Atlantic coast during the next six years:

1993	1994	1995	1996	1997	1998
Arlene	Alberto	Allison	Arthur	Ana	
Bret	Beryl	Barry	Bertha	Bill	Bonnie
Cindy	Chris	Chantal	Cesar	Claudette	Charley
Dennis	Debby	Dean	Dolly	Danny	Danielle
Emily	Ernesto	Erin	Edouard	Erika	Earl
Floyd	Florence	Felix	Fran	Fabian	Frances
Gert	Gordon	Gabrielle	Gustav	Grace	Georges
Harvey	Helene	Humberto	Hortense	Henri	Hermine
Irene	Issac	Iris	Isidore	Isabel	Ivan
Jose	Joyce	Jerry	Josephine	Juan	Jeanne
Katrina	Keith	Karen	Klaus	Kate	Karl
Lenny	Leslie	Luis	Lili	Larry	Lisa
Maria	Michael	Marilyn	Marco	Mindy	Mitch
Nate	Nadine	Noel	Nana	Nicholas	Nicole
Ophelia	Oscar	Opal	Omar	Odette	Otto
Philippe	Patty	Pablo	Paloma	Peter	Paula
Rita	Rafael	Roxanne	Rene	Rose	Richard
Stan	Sandy	Sebastien	Sally	Sam	Shary
Tammy	Tony	Tanya	Teddy	Teresa	Tomas
Vince	Valerie	Van	Vicky	Victor	Virginie
Wilma	William	Wendy	Wilfred	Wanda	Walter

WHY AND WHEN WE SEE RAINBOWS

MANY PEOPLE CONSIDER THE RAINBOW TO BE THE MOST magnificent of all sky phenomena. Its appearance has delighted children and inspired artists, poets and composers throughout the ages. In many cultures, notably the Irish, the rainbow was believed to be a magical pathway to good fortune and happy times. Although the ancient Greeks saw it as a sign of war and death, several cultures revered it as a symbol of renewed hope. In the Bible, the rainbow is a reminder that God will never again flood the earth. Indeed, a rainbow often is a sign that the rain has ended.

❈ Rainbows usually have only a fleeting existence, but on August 14, 1979, a rainbow was seen on the coast of North Wales that lasted for three hours — perhaps a world record.

A rainbow is merely sunlight. There is nothing material about it; it is an optical illusion like a mirage or a halo. To see a rainbow the proper angle must be set up between the sun and you, the observer, through an intervening curtain of rain. In other words, you must face the rain with the sun at your back; a rainbow cannot be formed if the sky is completely obscured by cloud. If one appears, it will be at a 42° angle up from your shadow.

This position — back to the sun while facing a shower — is the basis for the old weather adage that says a morning rainbow warns of foul weather, and an afternoon or evening rainbow promises clear skies. This bit of weatherlore relies on the usual west-to-east movement of weather systems in the mid-latitudes. Thus, if a rainbow is seen in the morning when the sun is to the east of where you stand, then the shower responsible for the rainbow must be to the west, and is likely moving towards you. On the other hand, if a rainbow is in the east in the afternoon or evening, then the rain has passed by and will continue to recede eastward, giving way to clearing skies from the west.

❈ In the tropics, where storms often travel from east to west, afternoon rainbows are often seen before a storm arrives.

Raindrops act like miniature prisms and mirrors, splitting light into a spectrum of colours from violet to red, and then reflecting those colours. Whether you see bright bands of colour depends on the angle at which the white sunlight strikes the surface of a raindrop. Part of the light is reflected and part of it enters the drop, where it is twice refracted, or bent, and once reflected.

The first refraction takes place when the light enters the drop and disperses into colours. On entry, the speed of the ray of light is slowed; in fact, each colour of light is slowed at a different rate and bent at a slightly different angle. Violet light travels the slowest and thus is curved the most. Red travels the fastest and is bent the least. When it reaches the opposite side of the drop, most of the light passes through. The remainder is reflected off the inside back of the drop and then is refracted again on leaving from the same side it entered. The angle between the entering sunlight and the exiting rainbow rays varies from 42° for red light to about 40° for violet light.

❄ The well-known weather proverb:
*A rainbow in the morning is the shepherd's warning
A rainbow at night is the shepherd's delight* is reliable about 65 percent of the time.

The geometry involved in the formation of rainbows means that those viewed from the ground, when the sun is just above the horizon, will appear as semicircles. The higher the sun is in the sky, the smaller the rainbow, disappearing altogether for someone on the ground when the sun is at an altitude of 42° above the horizon. A full-circle rainbow is rarely seen, although it may be visible from an airplane when the sun is high in the sky and reflecting off a curtain of rain. Well-defined, bright rainbows are associated with large raindrops. Coloration and definition are generally poor with small drops; for example, fog droplets produce pale, white bows.

Each raindrop disperses the full spectrum of colours, but you will see only a single colour from each drop, depending on the precise angle of the sunlight and your

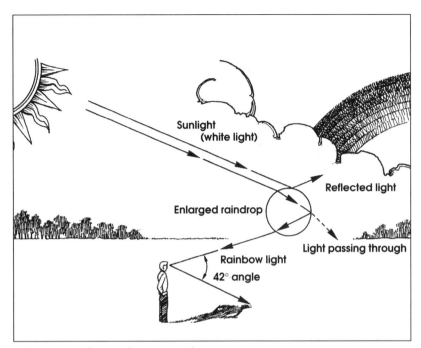

The process that produces a rainbow.

position. For instance, if orange light from a particular raindrop reaches your eyes, the red from that drop will fall toward the ground in front of you while the green light will pass above your head. You will see green light from raindrops at a lower altitude and blue from still lower drops.

It takes millions of falling raindrops — each refracting and reflecting light back to our eyes at slightly different angles — to produce the continuous coloured bands of the rainbow. As each drop falls, another takes its place in your line of vision, until the number of raindrops begins to diminish and the rainbow fades. The foot of the rainbow is its brightest spot; the seven colours — violet, indigo, blue, green, yellow, orange and red — blend at that point into a yellowish "pot of gold."

A facet of rainbows that adds to their universal appeal is that each person sees his or her own personal rainbow. While two people may admire the beauty of a rainbow together, what they see is not exactly the same, since each person views sunlight dispersed from a different set of raindrops. Everywhere you move, light from a different set of drops enters your eyes. Chasing rainbows, by the way, does not bring you any closer to them. A rainbow is as near or as far as the raindrops reflecting the sunlight.

When a bright rainbow is visible, a second, larger rainbow sometimes can be seen parallel to the first. The secondary bow occurs when sunlight enters the raindrops at a specific angle that allows light to make two reflections instead of one at the back of the raindrop. The colours are still refracted at slightly different angles, but those of the sec-ondary bow emerge from the drop at an angle of approximately 51°, not 42° as for the primary rainbow. This is why the sec-ondary bow is larger and is positioned above the original bow. It is also fainter because each reflection weakens the intensity of the light leaving the drop. Colours in the outer bow are in the reverse order to those in the primary rainbow, with red on the inside and violet on the outside. Three or more rainbows can occur, but they are usually too faint to be seen. With each additional reflection, there is a reversal of the previous order of colours.

❋ Rainbows occa-sionally occur on clear moonlit nights in the same way as daytime rainbows. However, because the light from the moon is dimmer than the sun's, lunar rainbows, or moon-bows, are notice-ably fainter and more difficult to see.

Honolulu, Hawaii, is famous for its brilliant rainbows; at Niagara Falls, visitors are treated to coloured arcs in the misty spray when the sun is shining. But one does not have to travel far to view a rainbow. Miniature coloured arches can be seen in the mist of water sprinklers, fountains and waterfalls, in the splash of a boat's bow wave, or in spray thrown up on a wet road. You can even see rainbows inside the drops of heavy dew lying on a lawn or hanging from a spider's web.

> ❄ Rainbows always appear in the opposite side of the sky from the sun.

In southern Canada, spectacular rainbows are seen most frequently in summer, because there are more showers and thunderstorms then, usually in the early morning or late afternoon. Rainbows are much less frequent in northern Canada, where there are fewer showers and thunderstorms.

NATURE'S SILENT FIREWORKS

FOR ANYONE WHO ENJOYS WATCHING THE NIGHT SKY, one of the greatest rewards is undoubtedly a shimmering display of northern lights, an unearthly luminescence that transforms the night sky into a painter's palette.

The aurora borealis can shine almost any day and night of the year, but it is most visible on cool, clear nights — especially between October and March — away from the background light of towns and cities.

This phenomenon can appear in many shapes and colours, but it often occurs in the early evening, between seven and 10 o'clock, as a thin veil of pale green light curving low across the sky like a monochrome rainbow. The arc or arcs of light sometimes last for hours, hanging motionless in the sky. Around midnight, however, the aurora may become more animated and colourful. It may develop folds, or pleats, called "rays" that dangle like curtains or ribbons, now dancing, now quivering rhythmically as the light brightens, then dims. As the tempo increases, shooting rays of red and reddish purple fill the sky, moving at about 100 metres per second.

At times the rays seem to be within arm's reach or, as one observer commented, "swirling through the bushes." Yet the closest the aurora comes to the earth's surface is 65 kilometres — about 10 times higher than the highest cloud — with the upper limit rarely extending beyond 1,000 kilometres. It is confined generally to the region of the atmosphere known as the ionosphere.

❄ According to the Oxford Dictionary, the term *aurora borealis* was introduced by French philosopher Gassendi in 1621. The oldest scientific report on the aurora was published in 1774 by Benjamin Franklin.

With the approach of morning, the pulsating streamers of light give way to long isolated streaks, and the aurora becomes patchy and pale. Then, as the sun rises, the aurora disappears from view because it is dimmer than the daylight.

The aurora's spectacular parade of light has fascinated northern peoples since ancient times and inspired many imaginative explanations of its origins. An Estonian folk tale likens the aurora to an enormous wedding in the sky with guests arriving on luminous sleighs, while an Inuit legend describes it as the torches held by new spirits to light their way to the heavens. Another Inuit tale suggests that the lights are the souls of their ancestors running across the snow during a game played with a walrus skull and a ball. And although some Inuit welcomed the lights and whistled to draw the soul closer, others whistled them away, fearing evil might befall them.

Scientists too have long been curious about the cause of the northern lights. During the early years of scientific inquiry, auroras were thought to be anything from sunlight reflecting off schools of herring or polar ice and snow, to sunlight leaking around the edges of the world. Since then, research has shown that, although the ultimate source of the lights is the sun, it is not sunlight itself we are seeing but other forms of electromagnetic energy.

The sun is constantly emitting a powerful stream of electrically charged particles, or solar wind that travels at supersonic speed, reaching the earth in two or three days. When the flow of particles approaches the earth, it is drawn toward the north and south magnetic poles by the earth's magnetic field. Like a river current flowing around a midstream rock, the particles form a teardrop-shaped magnetic field — the magnetosphere — around the earth.

The bombardment of the magnetosphere by high-energy solar particles, referred to as a geomagnetic storm, suddenly disturbs the earth's magnetic field. This disturbance creates a gigantic electrical generator that produces up to 10 million megawatts of electrical power. As the charged particles are drawn toward the north and south magnetic poles, they move closer to the earth's surface where the atmosphere is denser, and the chance of them colliding with atoms or molecules of atmospheric gases increases dramatically. The collisions energize the gases, creating a glowing light similar to that produced by the gas in a neon sign.

Because each atmospheric gas — mainly nitrogen, oxygen and hydrogen — generates a different colour, the colour of the aurora depends on which gases the charged particles collide with and the amount of energy released.

❋ Early postulations as to what causes the aurora: radium, torchlights, angels' wings, reflected light from polar ice fields, light from demons' lanterns, electricity in clouds that was released over the poles once the clouds condensed as snow, vapours from northern volcanoes, and reflections off huge herring runs or whales thrashing in the waves.

Hydrogen molecules, for example, glow red when struck by the particles, while hydrogen atoms radiate green light. Ionized nitrogen generates blue or purple light, and neutral nitrogen radiates pink or purplish red light. The brightest and most common auroral displays, a pale yellow green, occur when the particles strike the very cold oxygen atoms at altitudes between 100 and 150 kilometres. At an altitude of 250 kilometres, near the limit of human vision, a collision with oxygen atoms produces red light.

In regions where the northern lights are rarely seen, they have been mistaken for everything from fires to UFOs. In 1938, a particularly brilliant display of red northern lights visible in England caused firefighters to race to Windsor Castle in the belief it was burning.

Contrary to popular belief, the North Pole is not the best place in the world to view the aurora borealis. The best places lie along a path called the northern auroral oval, which encircles the north magnetic pole. In Canada, the oval encompasses much of the Yukon and the southern Northwest Territories, dipping south over northern Alberta, Saskatchewan, Manitoba and Ontario, then curving north again over northern Quebec and Labrador.

From these locations, the odds of seeing the northern lights are almost two nights out of every three, whereas people living along the 49th parallel may see them perhaps 30 nights a year. Torontonians, for example, can expect to see the aurora borealis an average of 18 nights a year. In Yellowknife, the number is 243; Churchill, Manitoba, 190; Fort St. John, British Columbia, 125; Goose Bay, Newfoundland, 100; Prince Albert, Saskatchewan, 95; Edmonton, 90; Winnipeg, 75; Ottawa, 35; and Halifax,

❋ Aurora-weather folklore: southerly winds and a storm will come within 48 hours following northern lights.

20. Of course these figures are based on the presumption that observers would be watching the sky all night, every night and that it would be clear. As it happens, in the fall and winter there is cloud cover from 45 to 65 percent of the time, making it impossible to see the aurora from the surface of the earth.

Auroral displays occur often, but because they are more brilliant during periods of increased solar activity, they are more obvious then. Every 11 years or so, the surface of the sun reaches a peak in activity. At such times, the auroral display may take place night and day and may be seen over wide regions of the earth. The period 1989–90 had an increased frequency, and more displays can be expected around the year 2001.

A common misconception about the northern lights is that they influence day-to-day weather changes. The Roman poet, Virgil, suggested that brilliant displays of the aurora signal approaching cold weather. Mariners have long believed that they are harbingers of bad weather. In Scotland, it is commonly said that "the first great aurora of the fall is followed by a storm in two days." Today meteorologists believe that the northern lights have nothing to do with the weather now, tomorrow or next week. People in Schefferville, Quebec, and Thompson, Manitoba, may all see the same northern lights, but their local weather may be quite different. In the far north, the aurora can be seen almost every night, weather permitting.

Retired Canadian meteorologist Rube Hornstein has

❄ The Geophysics Division of the Geological Survey of Canada has been issuing forecasts of geomagnetic storms and auroral activity to power companies, communication facilities, defense officials and individuals since 1974. The Canadian Magnetic Observatory consists of 13 observatories. At present the Canadian forecasting service issues three types of geomagnetic forecasts: medium-term (27 day multi-zone forecasts); short-term (72 hour forecasts); and magnetic alert messages.

contended that associating spectacular auroral displays with a spell of fine cold weather is readily understandable. The aurora can be seen in most places only on clear starlit nights, when radiation cooling usually occurs at the earth's surface. Chances are the next morning will also be crisp, cool and fine. However, it is equally likely that a similarly bright display could be shining on an overcast warm night, but we obviously would not be able to see it because of the cloud cover. Thus, although cold weather favours viewing the northern lights, the aurora's appearance or non-appearance has no connection with cold weather or any other kind of weather.

> ❄ The power of the northern lights can sometimes generate in excess of 1 trillion watts of electricity in the atmosphere, equal to the rate of the electric generation of all the power plants in the United States.

That weather should be linked with solar disturbances is understandable — after all, the sun is the only source of energy for driving weather and sustaining life on earth. Indeed, countless studies claim success in correlating sunspot frequency with the occurrence of weather changes, the rotary motion of storms and weather abnormalities. However, for every claim of sunspot-weather correlation, there is denial or counterclaim. The truth is that much more is guessed at than is known. Any genuine link between solar activity, auroral display and the weather must await further scientific scrutiny. Not only must weather forecasters wait for more credible evidence, but so must others contending that links exist between solar cycles and stock-market fluctuations, flu epidemics, the number of polar bears, the length of women's dresses, psychological moods and the quality of vintage wines.

Another common belief is that the northern lights make noise. People viewing the aurora often claim they can hear a faint rustling or crackling sound like the hum of an electric transformer. All efforts to record these sounds have failed, and even if the aurora did make noise, it would not be audible from the earth's surface. The air at 100 kilometres up is so thin that it cannot transmit sound waves. One theory suggests that the hissing sounds may be from ice crystals forming as the observer breathes into very cold air, and the rustling may be from minute sparks emitted by trees or bushes in the highly charged electric field that exists at ground level during the geomagnetic storms that cause the aurora borealis.

Beautiful and inspiring as the northern lights may be, the geomagnetic storms associated with them are a major problem for communications companies and utilities. The electrical energy flowing to the earth below the lights is powerful enough to alter radio transmissions, distort television reception, cross telephone conversations, disrupt radar systems, trigger burglar alarms and activate automatic garage doors. Large bursts of auroral activity have also played havoc with electrical systems by overloading utility circuits and causing widespread blackouts. In March 1989, an auroral superstorm overloaded utility circuits in Eastern Canada, causing intense power surges that left Montreal and large parts of Quebec blacked out for as long as nine hours.

❉ Homing pigeons' ability to navigate is impaired during intense aurora.

Auroral scientists issue forecasts of auroral activity about one or two hours in advance of the display, much like meteorologists issue weather forecasts. However, unlike weather forecasters, they cannot predict aurora two or more days in advance. Solar eruptions occur without warning. The lag between an eruption and the corresponding light display on earth may vary from two to 10 days. Even the sighting of a major solar flare does not allow them to predict an auroral display with any reliability, because no one can say for sure how close the solar winds will come to the earth.

Despite the damage and inconvenience inflicted by auroral storms, nature's solar-powered light show continues to evoke the same awe and wonderment in us as it did in our ancestors.

LIGHTNING — DAZZLING AND DEADLY

L IGHTNING IS THE MOST FRIGHTENING AND SPECTACU-lar weather phenomenon most of us ever see. In the tiny fraction of a second it takes for lightning to ignite, a bolt of lightning travels at half the speed of light and scorches the surrounding air to a temperature five times hotter than the sun's surface. A single stroke can be as short as 50 metres, or as long as 30 kilometres, and deliver a current of electricity between 10,000 and 100,000 amps. Although we have not learned everything about lightning, we have come a long way since the Middle Ages, when church bells were rung in fruitless attempts to disperse the celestial bolts. The practice was abandoned after hundreds of bell ringers were electrocuted.

❋ Lightning can travel at a speed of 140,000 kilometres per second. At that speed, a rocket could reach the moon in less than three seconds.

These days, lightning is responsible for about 15 deaths a year in Canada, more than any other stormy weather event. No one hit directly by lightning lives to tell about it. Packing 10,000 times the current used in the electric

---

SOME LIGHTNING MYTHS

- Thunderstorms and lightning turn milk sour.
- Noisy thunderstorms will cause the young buds on trees to grow faster.
- Lightning never strikes the same place twice.
- Animals draw lightning.
- Open doors and windows invite lightning to come inside.
- Rubber tires make vehicle occupants safe from lightning. (It is the steel frame that protects people in cars and trucks.)

---

chair, lightning can fry skin and explode internal organs. Most victims are struck while outdoors in the peak thunderstorm period of late afternoon, often while seeking shelter under a tall tree. Indirect strikes, from lightning that hits a nearby target and travels along the ground or through the air, cause countless more serious injuries ranging from shock and burns to paralysis and blindness. Fortunately, about two-thirds of the people injured reportedly make a full recovery.

Although science is still unable to explain exactly how the electrical charge builds up so rapidly in clouds, the forces at work can be explained. Lightning is simply a giant spark in the sky, not unlike the static electricity you experience while touching a metal object after shuffling across the carpet on a dry day. The earth's surface has a predominantly negative charge and the upper atmosphere an opposite, positive charge. During the development of a thundercloud, positive and negative electrical charges are carried into the cloud. Many

※ There is no such thing as heat lightning. What you are really seeing is diffused lightning from a distant thunderstorm, too far away (greater than 20 kilometres) to be heard.

❋ "Cats groom themselves before a storm." Thunderstorms generate static electricity, which separates a cat's coat hairs, making it feel dirty. Licking their coat smooths the hair.

mechanisms are involved that can lead to separating the charges, including in-cloud collisions between solid and liquid water particles, powerful updrafts and downdrafts within the cloud, and the splintering of charged ice crystals during the freezing of cloud droplets.

In simple terms, the storm cloud behaves like a giant storage battery. A high concentration of positively charged particles collects in the frozen upper layers of the cloud and a surplus of negatively charged particles collects at the base of the cloud. Because unlike charges attract each other, the negative charge at the bottom of the cloud induces a patch of positive charges to form on the ground directly beneath it. As the thunderstorm moves along, the region of positive charges follows it like an electrical shadow. Attracted by the cloud above, the currents in this "shadow" flow up any protruding objects such as trees, flagpoles, buildings and people. Air, however, is a poor conductor, so the current cannot flow up easily from ground to cloud.

In well-developed clouds, a tremendous difference grows in the electrical potential between the upper and lower regions within the cloud, and between the ground and the cloud base. When this potential reaches about a billion volts, the insulating air can resist no longer. A giant spark slashes out in a series of connected events measured in milliseconds. It begins with a leader, a nearly invisible stream of negatively charged particles that extends earthward from the cloud. The leader travels in a series of short, often zigzagging steps about 50 metres long, pausing for

❋ In April 1992, three skiers on Vail Mountain in Colorado were injured, one critically, when a lightning bolt struck the top of their chair lift.

some 50-millionths of a second between each branch. In its wake, it leaves a pencil-thin path of ionized air, the conducting channel that the main stroke of lightning will follow. When the leader is within about 100 metres of the ground, the ground streamer (with its net positive charge) leaps up to meet it. As soon as the pathway between ground and cloud is complete, the visible lightning flashes along it: a highly energetic and luminous return stroke that surges upward from the ground. That's right — visible lightning travels up, not down.

After the main stroke, electrical charges build up again in as little as 50 milliseconds, and additional strokes, called dart leaders, can flash down and up the same conducting channel. Often three or four dart leaders will flash in a multiple discharge lasting for a quarter of a second or more, continuing until the charge is neutralized or the wind breaks up the electrified channel. Although the bright return strokes travel from the ground to the cloud, it happens so quickly that the whole channel appears to flash simultaneously. This entire process consumes less than a second of time.

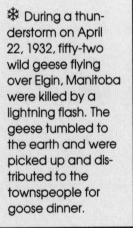

✳ During a thunderstorm on April 22, 1932, fifty-two wild geese flying over Elgin, Manitoba were killed by a lightning flash. The geese tumbled to the earth and were picked up and distributed to the townspeople for goose dinner.

Where there's lightning, there's thunder, unless you are more than 20 kilometres away and out of range of the sound. Thunder happens when the air along the lightning channel is seared momentarily to an incandescent white heat of 30,000°C. This forces the air column to expand suddenly into the surrounding air, creating a booming shock wave that becomes the sound wave called thunder. Because light travels about a million times faster than sound, we see the lightning almost the instant it occurs, but we hear the thunder later. By counting the number of seconds

---

SOME LIGHTNING SAFETY RULES

- Check the latest weather forecast and keep an eye on the sky.
- Stay indoors, away from open doors and windows, fireplaces and electrical appliances. Do not use phones, showers or baths.
- If you are outdoors, do not make yourself into a lightning rod by projecting yourself above the surrounding terrain; do not stand near possible lightning conductors such as trees and utility poles.
- You are safe inside a car, provided you do not touch any metal parts.
- Move away from open water — swimming pools, lakes and rivers. If you are in a small boat, go ashore.
- Stay away from metal objects such as clotheslines, wire fences, rails, golf carts, bicycles and farm machinery.
- Do not carry tools, umbrellas, golf clubs, fishing rods and other metal objects. Take off metal-cleated golf shoes.
- If you are with a group in the open, all spread out.

---

between seeing the lightning and hearing its thunder, and dividing by three you can calculate your distance from the lightning in kilometres. For example, if you wait 12 seconds between seeing a lightning flash and hearing a thunderclap, the storm is about four kilometres away.

Each year in Canada, several hundred million lightning bolts strike the ground. Around the world, at any given moment, an estimated 2,000 thunderstorms are active, spawning 100 lightning strikes and hundreds more flashes per second. Their distribution is not even; lightning is much less frequent over the oceans than over

❄ Santa's (rain) deer were named Donner (thunder) and Blitzen (lightning).

land, and uncommon in the high Arctic. The number of lightning strikes is not recorded in detail in Canada, but a rough estimate can be obtained by adding up the hours of thunderstorms observed at Canadian airports. Windsor may be Canada's lightning capital, averaging 53 thunderstorm hours a year. The area between Thunder Bay and Winnipeg

❄ It would take 200 million trumpeters blowing for 13 seconds to produce the acoustic energy in a good crack of thunder.

experiences about 45 to 50 thunderstorm hours a year, with the rest of the West between 25 and 40. The West Coast has fewer than five a year, whereas the Atlantic region has between 10 and 20. The count drops rapidly with latitude: over most of the northern boreal forest there are fewer than ten thunderstorm hours per year. Outside Canada, the most active area in North America is Tampa, Florida, with 116 hours.

Lightning starts 40 percent of the forest fires in Canada and is the most frequent reason for power blackouts. It is not all bad, though. Were it not for lightning, the planet would lose its electrical charge in a matter of minutes. Lightning provides half of the earth's supply of natural fertilizer. The bolt is the catalyst that unites airborne nitrogen with oxygen to form ozone, ammonia and oxides of nitrogen. These compounds react with rainwater to produce soluble fertilizers.

There are no completely safe havens from lightning; however, the risk can be greatly minimized if you know where to go and what to do. During a thunderstorm, when your hair stands on end, your skin tingles, or you take on a blue glow or halo, a lightning strike may be only seconds away. In this event, immediately drop to your knees and bend

❄ Over a recent 10-year period, 380 Australians were killed or injured by lightning while talking on the telephone during a thunderstorm.

forward so that your head is lower than your back. Put your hands on your thighs, but don't let your head touch the ground. Don't lie flat on the ground. People struck by lightning receive an electrical shock and may be burned, but they carry no electrical charge. Resuscitation should be started immediately.

JET STREAMS: FAST-FLOWING RIVERS OF AIR

HIGH ABOVE THE EARTH'S SURFACE, A BAND OF WIND called the jet stream meanders from west to east like a writhing snake. Travelling at different speeds in the westerlies, this large band of air has weaker currents that run alongside and sometimes join the main, faster flow to form a great river of air. The core of the jet has sharp boundaries, confined like a river within its banks. It speeds up and slows down as it moves along, altering the weather as it changes its course.

> ❋ An airplane heading into a 160 kilometre per hour jet steam on a trip from Halifax to Vancouver would take about an hour longer than a trip going in the same direction as the jet stream.

For meteorologists, the jet stream (actually there are several) is one of the keys to forecasting tomorrow's weather. These strong upper winds can move air masses into and out of an area and promote the development of storms or fine weather. Its position can explain why Texas freezes under a cold snap while Montreal warms up with a thaw, or why Edmonton can be bitterly cold one week and abnormally mild the next.

Sky watchers first became aware of the jet stream at the beginning of this century when they observed the rapid movement of clouds at altitudes of six to eight kilometres. In the 1920s and 1930s, scientists confirmed its existence by launching weather balloons. But it was not until the end of World War II that meteorologists made their first detailed observations of these powerful winds.

> ❄ Tremendous speeds have been observed in the jet stream: 200 kilometres per hour is commonplace, 300 is not unusual, and values as high as 400 have been reported.

Pilots flying high-altitude aircraft over Japan and the Mediterranean during the war also brought back first-hand accounts of the jet stream. At times they encountered head winds so strong that they could make no ground speed at all — their airplanes virtually stood still in midair. On several occasions, a B-29 bomber squadron had to abort its mission over Japanese-occupied islands and jettison bomb loads into the sea. When they turned around and flew east — the same direction as the jet stream — the pilots found they were covering ground at twice the indicated air speed.

Typically, the jet stream circles the earth between eight and 14 kilometres above the ground, depending on the latitude and season. It is two to four kilometres deep, between 50 and 150 kilometres wide and a few thousand kilometres long. Speeds at the jet core occasionally reach 400 kilometres an hour, but on average, jet winds blow over North America at between 100 and 200 kilometres per hour, circling the globe in about five days.

Like all winds, the jet stream is caused by the contrast in temperature between warm and cold air, which in turn creates a difference in air pressure. Air pressure, or barometric pressure, is simply the weight of an entire air column above the earth surface. Usually the higher you go, the less air there is overhead and the lower the pressure. It decreases more rapidly with increasing altitude in cold air than in warm air. To compensate for this difference, air moves from areas of high pressure associated with warmer air to areas of lower pressure associated with colder air, creating wind. The greater the contrast in temperature and pressure between two air masses, the stronger the winds will be. The temperature difference between polar and tropical regions averages about 30°C in summer, but may exceed 70°C in winter. Consequently, the winter jet stream travels almost twice as fast as the summer jet.

During November 1–3, 1991, a powerful early winter jet coincided with a storm that brought the season's first major snowfall to southern Manitoba and northwestern Ontario. Over Lake Superior, the temperature five kilometres above the surface was –30°C, while over Pittsburgh, Pennsylvania, the temperature at the same altitude was –13°C. This temperature difference over a relatively short distance produced a strong jet stream above the Great Lakes with winds exceeding 185 kilometres an hour.

❋ The jet stream can be accurately located by examining satellite cloud pictures. Cirrus clouds predominate on the equatorial side of the jet stream. The poleward side is often cloud-free. The cirrus lies under the jet axis, and frequently casts a shadow on the lower clouds which is clearly visible in satellite pictures.

Usually there are several jet stream systems winding around the earth, sometimes in a discontinuous band, and other times completely encircling the globe. Now and then they branch into two or three streams, only to merge as a stronger jet downwind.

There are two major jets in the Northern Hemisphere. The polar jet — popularized by television weather forecasters as the ribbon of air that sweeps across North America bringing tomorrow's weather — is located at the boundary between cold air to the north and warm air to the south. Another jet, the subtropical jet, is centred at 25° north latitude during the Northern Hemisphere

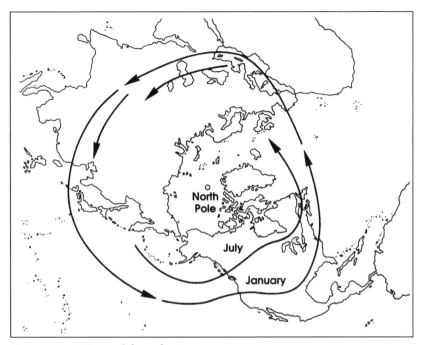

Average positions of the polar jet stream.

winter at an average height of about 12 kilometres. It is generally less energetic and less variable than its northern counterpart and, consequently, has little direct effect on our weather.

In summer, the average location of the polar jet stream over central Canada is about 50° north latitude. In winter, it may arc northward over British Columbia and then turn sharply southward over the Great Plains. It may plunge as far south as northern Texas before recurving north-eastward over the Mississippi River valley. Finally, it wends its way eastward and leaves North America over New England or Atlantic Canada.

The jet stream exerts a considerable influence on our everyday weather. It is associated with the movement of masses of air in and out of Canada, the strengthening of storms, and the steering of low and high pressure centres. As a general rule, when the jet stream is to the south, cold air pushes downward from the north, and when the jet stream is to the north, weather often comes from the west or south.

At times the jet stream follows the lines of latitude, driving masses of mild, moist air from the Pacific Ocean all the way across Canada. This flow is zonal, and is associated with usually moderate and changeable weather. Other times, the jet resembles a roller coaster, looping far to the north then plunging southward. This flow is meridional. It can spread a blanket of frigid arctic air over the central portion of North America from the North Pole to the Gulf of Mexico, and push mild air from the Gulf of Mexico or the Caribbean over the eastern seaboard. This north-south movement also helps form storms with brisk winds and copious amounts of rain or snow. Sometimes, the jet stream blocks the normal eastward movement of weather. It is not unusual under such circumstances to have a cold or warm spell that lasts several weeks, with only brief interruptions.

❄ The strong vertical wind shears — changes in wind speed at different altitudes — that often occur in the vicinity of the jet streams may cause the violent overturning of air known as clear air turbulence. Besides being a hazard to passengers and crew, turbulence puts stress on aircraft bodies, reducing their useful life.

The jet stream also assists in the formation of storm systems, or cyclones, and intensifies thunderstorms and tornadoes. At certain points along the jet stream, air diverges outwards, thus reducing the total weight of air from the top of the atmosphere down to the ground. With corresponding lower pressures at the surface and an inward flow of air to fill the partial vacuum at its centre, a low pressure area forms. Once a storm develops, its direction and speed are largely determined by the orientation and intensity of the upper-level jet.

Jet streams are both a boon and a bane to pilots flying transcontinental and intercontinental routes. Pilots can reduce flight times by making use of the jet streams when flying east or by avoiding them when heading west. A westbound flight from Toronto to Vancouver might take four hours and 30 minutes, whereas the return flight will probably take under four hours. Pilots can also save fuel by planning their flight paths carefully in order to utilize as much tail wind — and avoid as much head wind — as possible. The air temperature en route is also important because the efficiency of jet engines decreases with increasing outside temperatures. In the Toronto–Vancouver–Toronto example, westward flight paths that go above or around the jet stream and eastward flights that ride the jet stream save anywhere from 10 to 20 percent in fuel costs. Such flight planning saves money by improving fuel efficiency and by freeing extra fuel space for passengers and cargo.

Time and economic savings are not the only, nor the prime, consideration in planning flight operations. In-flight safety is of paramount importance. Not surprisingly, turbulence, icing and storms are avoided as much as possible. Near the jet stream core, strong wind shears (rapid changes of wind velocity over short distances) may cause the violent overturning of air currents, causing a bumpy flight. The turbulence occurs in layers of air 400 to 600 metres thick, so a pilot can get out of it merely by changing altitude. In extreme cases and over a long time, turbulence can lead to material fatigue and even to aircraft failure.

The next time you see a forecaster pointing out a meandering jet stream on a weather map, or an airline captain announcing he or she will be "catching the jet" at 9,000 metres (30,000 feet), you will know they are both talking about the same fast-flowing river of air.

BLAME IT ON EL NIÑO

O VER THE YEARS, A WIDE RANGE OF SEVERE OR BIZARRE weather anomalies have been blamed on El Niño, a pronounced warming of the Pacific Ocean current off the coast of South America. That was the case in 1992 when, rightly or wrongly, this well-known but little-understood phenomenon was linked to August snow-storms in Alberta, dust storms and bush fires in Australia, starving sea lions off California, mud slides in Utah, rat-tlesnake infestations in Texas, the deaths of tens of mil-lions of monarch butterflies in Mexico, snowstorms in Jerusalem, and a deep economic recession everywhere.

A decade earlier, the landmark El Niño of 1982–83 — one of the strongest and costliest on record — was blamed for the worst drought in Australia in two centuries, star-vation and mass migration in drought-striken Africa, and flooding rains in Brazil and Paraguay. It reduced life-giving monsoon rains in India, Indonesia and the Philippines, and spawned the first typhoon to strike French Polynesia in 75 years, followed by five more in five months.

For centuries, Ecuadoran and Peruvian fishermen used the term El Niño (Spanish for "the boy child" or, by impli-cation, the Christ-child) to describe a weak, warm ocean current that arrived each year around Christmas, adversely affecting their catches. In some years, however, an unexplained reversal in atmospheric circulation over the South Pacific and Indian oceans causes the current to warm even more — from 2°C to 5°C above the average maximum sea-surface temperature of 28°C — and

❋ Particularly strong El Niños occurred in 1891, 1899-1990, 1925-26, 1931, 1941-42, 1957–58, 1965, 1972-73, 1976-77, 1982-83, 1986 and 1992.

48

expand to cover an area up to three times the size of Canada. The effect of this pronounced warming on the world's weather is so dramatic that today the name El Niño is primarily reserved for such exceptional events.

> ❄ El Niño is technically "a transitory irregularity in the global ocean-atmospheric system."

Known to Spanish explorers of Latin America nearly 400 years ago, El Niño was not recognized as part of a global system leading to droughts in some regions and torrential rains in others until the middle of the 20th century. Today, climatologists have still not determined exactly what triggers the process that produces El Niño. Everything from stiffening trade winds and water piling up in the western Pacific, to changes in the salt content of the oceans and heat from lava spewing from undersea volcanoes has been suggested. However, considerable insight has been gained into the chain of events leading up to this unusual warming trend.

The changes in ocean circulation that produce El Niño have been linked to what is called the Southern Oscillation, a giant seesaw pattern of atmospheric pressure between the eastern and western tropical Pacific. Most of the time, the equatorial trade winds blow west, from a persistent high-pressure system over the southeastern tropical Pacific near Tahiti, toward an equally persistent low-pressure system parked over Indonesia and northern Australia. This westward flow of air drags warm surface water westward, raising sea levels off the coasts of Indonesia and northern Australia by 30 to 70 centimetres and turning the western Pacific into an immense storehouse of energy. Meanwhile, on the other side of the Pacific, offshore winds along the South American coast strip away the shallow surface waters, causing an upwelling of cold, nutrient-rich water.

The equatorial trade winds mysteriously slacken or

❄ El Niño can set in at almost any time of the year; however, it usually occurs early in the calendar year. By about August, it is generally possible to determine whether this event is underway.

change direction in an El Niño year, flowing east instead of west. No longer supported by the trade winds, the giant underwater wave that has accumulated in the western Pacific sloshes back towards the coast of South America, much like water in a bathtub. This warm eastward countercurrent becomes stronger as it makes its way back across the Pacific. On its 2½-month journey, it also becomes warmer under the hot tropical sun. Eventually, it reaches its destination and overrides the normal upwelling of cold water off the coasts of Peru and Ecuador.

The changes in oceanic and atmospheric circulation associated with El Niño cause atypical weather patterns around the world. Rising heat and moisture from the ocean off Peru and Ecuador provide the raw energy for more frequent storms and torrential rainfalls over these normally arid countries. In Canada and the northern United States, the additional heat strengthens and alters the path of the jet stream, the high-altitude, fast-moving river of air that steers weather systems around the world. A diverted jet stream can wreak havoc with the weather wherever it goes.

❄ The 1982–83 El Niño was blamed for some 1,500 weather-related deaths and up to $10 billion in damages worldwide.

What happens to North American weather in the weeks following the onset of El Niño largely depends on whether the jet stream remains a single stream or splits in two. A single jet stream, curving north over British Columbia then plunging south through the centre of the continent, brings colder temperatures to the Great Lakes region and eastern North America. At the same time, a high-pressure system stalls over the Rocky Mountains, preventing moist Pacific air from moving inland. Mild dry weather then dominates Western Canada and the northwestern United States.

If the jet stream splits, its northern branch tends to create storms in the Gulf of Alaska and warm temperatures in Western Canada. Its southern branch delivers storms to California, Texas and Florida before moving up the east coast of North America.

Regardless of which path the jet stream takes, it is difficult to predict what type of weather an El Niño will bring to northeastern North America, because each occurrence varies greatly in strength and impact. In the winter of 1982–83, during that record El Niño, very mild Pacific air penetrated east to the Great Lakes and beyond. Yet six years earlier, during a weaker El Niño, southern Ontario had suffered a bitterly cold winter while the West basked in balmy temperatures.

Every four to five years on average, a pool of cooler-than-normal water — as much as 2°C below the average maximum sea-surface temperature of 28°C — replaces the warm El Niño current off the western coast of South America. The effects of this cooler water, called La Niña, contrast sharply with those of El Niño. La Niña brings wetter monsoons to India, flooding to Bangladesh, colder winters to the Canadian West and Alaska, and drier, warmer weather to the American Southeast. There have been 20 La Niñas (Spanish for "the girl child") since 1885.

El Niño events are far from regular. They occur on average every three to five years, but the interval can vary

❄ Scientists at the University of Guelph in Guelph, Ontario, believe that the teeth of female dusky dolphins can be used to date the occurrence of El Niños. Dolphin teeth accumulate a new layer of dentine each year. In female duskies, the layer for El Niño is unusually thin, probably reflecting a shortage in food supplies.

✳ The earliest documents referring to El Niño date back to 1795 and are credited to a Captain Colonet. El Niño was first recognized as part of a giant ocean-atmosphere circulation pattern in the 1920s by Sir Gilbert Walker. The pattern is known as the Walker Circulation or the Southern Oscillation.

from two to 10 years. Typically, an El Niño lasts from 12 to 18 months; however, some expire within a few months.

El Niño can have both good and bad side effects. It can be good news for British Columbia salmon fishermen, as Fraser River–bound sockeye opt for the cooler waters of Johnstone Strait rather than the Strait of Juan de Fuca, making them available to Canadian fishermen only. On the other hand, schools of hungry mackerel riding the El Niño wave may devour young sockeye stock. For Prairie farmers, anxious to see soil moisture replenished, El Niño's usually snow-free winter is not welcome news. Yet an El Niño year also correlates with a warmer, wetter spring, which increases spring wheat yields. For birds and mammals foraging through crusty snow, El Niño can be a boon, but not for people who enjoy skiing and skating. For householders, El Niño mildness can mean significant savings resulting from reduced energy needs.

Although no two El Niños or their effects are exactly alike, what excites meteorologists everywhere is the sense that El Niño and the associated weather may be predictable a season or even a year in advance. The first step toward such a long-range forecast is deciding whether El Niño will continue to exert its global influence on the weather. Some work is already under way using satellites and shipboard instruments to monitor the key early warning signs of El Niño: surface water warming off the coast of Peru, shifts in the trade winds and differences in atmospheric pressure between Australia and the eastern Pacific. Whether or not it is possible to forecast the emergence of El Niño, it may be possible to get at least a few months' warning of an increased risk of weather-related disasters. But long-range forecasting is not easy and, so far, predictions are not reliable enough to be useful.

It may be another three to five years before the next El Niño makes the news. But when it does, chances are that we will all be in for another bout of weird, wild and woolly weather.

PLUGGING THE POLAR OZONE HOLES

THERE IS SOMETHING UTTERLY IMPROBABLE ABOUT THE survival of our planet being threatened by egg cartons, deodorant sprays, discarded refrigerators, hamburger containers, furniture padding and fire extinguishers. It sounds more like the plot for a B movie or a new "Air Farce" skit. Seldom, though, has an environmental issue evoked such public concern or such immediate action from government and industry as the polar ozone holes.

> ❄ If all ozone-depleting chemicals were successfully phased out, the ozone layer would eventually heal itself.

At ground level, ozone is a pollutant originating from the photochemical reaction between motor vehicle exhaust and sunlight. Surface ozone endangers human health, damages agricultural crops and is part of the suffocating smog over large urban areas. Paradoxically, ozone is the only gas in the atmosphere that shields us from overexposure to the sun's lethal ultraviolet (UV) radiation. Without this delicate filter, life on earth would be impossible.

❋ If you have ever noticed the sharp, clean smell after a thunderstorm or the "electric" smell of a subway train, you've smelled a bit of ozone gas. In larger amounts, ozone is unpleasant; its strong odour irritates the eyes and lungs.

Ozone is a bluish-coloured gas with the same pungent "clean" odour we often smell following a thunderstorm. About 90 percent of the ozone lies in the stratosphere, 15 to 35 kilometres above the earth. Scientists call it a trace constituent of the atmosphere, because it makes up only a few parts per million in a given volume of air. Squeezed together it would measure about three millimetres in depth, or about the thickness of two "loonies."

In nature there is a delicate balance between the amount of ozone created and the amount destroyed. Ozone forms when the sun's UV radiation bombards and breaks apart ordinary oxygen molecules. Once split, the freed oxygen atoms recombine with intact oxygen molecules to form ozone. Ozone molecules don't live for long, though. They too break up when they collide with other molecules or undergo UV radiation.

Man-made chemicals can also cause ozone breakdown. Chlorofluorocarbons (CFCs) are a family of synthetic chemicals, best known for their use as propellants in spray cans, coolant fluid in refrigerators and air conditioners, insulating foam-blowing agents, fire retardants and microchip cleaners. At ground level, CFCs are safe and stable. But when they drift up slowly and unimpeded to the frigid stratosphere, they too are zapped by the UV radiation and easily separate into their constituent parts of chlorine, fluorine and carbon. The chlorine molecule, in particular, has a voracious appetite. With the help of the sun, a single molecule can devour tens of thousands of ozone molecules, before

❋ Canada accounted for just under 2 percent of the world's supply of chlorofluorocarbons (CFCs) and halons in 1986.

being washed out of the stratosphere by rain. One of the major concerns about CFCs is their longevity: they remain in the atmosphere for hundreds of years. Even if emissions of these gases were banned tomorrow, replenishment of the lost ozone would take hundreds of years. In the meantime, more ozone holes are waiting to happen.

A British survey team broke the stunning news of a southern springtime ozone hole over the coldest part of the world in 1985. The members had observed a large crater-like hole about the size of Canada over Antarctica. The hole was not totally devoid of ozone; rather, it was a large area in which the concentration of the gas was half of what it had been a decade earlier. Equally important was the discovery in late 1988 of chlorine compounds in concentrations 500 to 600 times greater than normal at the altitude where the ozone depletion was the greatest. The Antarctic ozone hole was larger and thinner than ever before, and chlorine compounds were responsible.

> ✳ In a June 1993 Angus Reid/ Southam News poll, Canadians ranked the thinning ozone layer as our biggest environmental threat, followed by water pollution, air pollution, rain forest destruction and garbage.

High-altitude balloon profiles over Antarctica in September 1992 confirmed the worse predictions of scientists. The level of ozone was the lowest ever recorded at these uninhabited latitudes. The observations also confirmed that the South Pole ozone depletion started sooner and proceeded faster than in any previous year. Subsequent measurements taken by NASA satellites in October and November 1992 detected expansion of the antarctic ozone hole to a record size, nearly three times the size of Canada and 25 percent larger than in the past. Furthermore, the outer edge of the hole had shifted for the first time to a populated island off the southern tip of the South American mainland.

> ❊ Stratospheric ozone levels over Toronto and Edmonton have declined by about 4 percent since the late 1970s.

Many scientists believe that the ozone layer has worn thinner since 1991 due to the continued use of chemicals as well as the volcanic gases from Mount Pinatubo in the Philippines, which erupted in 1991 sending 25 million tonnes of sulphate aerosols into the stratosphere. They suspect that the volcanic debris is interacting with the industrial chemicals, leading to increased ozone depletion. Debris from major volcanic eruptions usually remains in the upper atmosphere for two to three years.

Long before this startling news, scientists from Environment Canada's weather service were measuring the chemistry and temperature of the arctic ozone layer, using rockets, satellites and helium-filled balloons. In the spring of 1986, Wayne Evans of the Atmospheric Environment Service first confirmed the existence of a thinning arctic ozone layer. In early 1989, based on measurements taken 800 kilometres from the North Pole, at Alert, Northwest Territories, he discovered a small hole over the Arctic. The northern hole proved much harder to detect than its southern counterpart. It was not as broad — about the size of Ontario and Quebec combined — or as deep as the antarctic hole. It also had a tendency

> ❊ Global supply of CFCs and halons declined by 31 percent, from an estimated 1,260 kilotonnes to 870 kilotonnes between 1986 and 1990.

to drift over the North Pole. From January to April 1993, Environment Canada scientists reported that the protective ozone layer over Canada was thinner than in any of the past 30 years that measurements have been taken. Record low springtime ozone values average 24 and 22 percent below the pre-1980 normal values over Toronto and Edmonton, respectively.

WHAT IS THE UV INDEX?

Developed by Canadian scientists, the UV (ultraviolet) index indicates the strength of the sun's UV rays under clear sky conditions.

The index levels range from 0 to 10. The higher the value, the more intense the ultraviolet radiation. For example, 10 is the typical UV level found at midday in the tropics. The UV levels change with the seasons and time of day.

UV Index	Category	Sunburn Time
over 9	extreme	less than 15 minutes
7–9	high	about 20 minutes
4–7	moderate	about 30 minutes
0–4	low	more than one hour

The same ozone-depleting process is at work over both poles, but because the air near the North Pole is warmer and therefore circulates more than the air near the South Pole, stratospheric ice crystals — those little platforms on which chemical interaction occurs — form less readily. Consequently, polar stratospheric clouds are not as prevalent in the Arctic, and ozone depletion is short-lived and less evident than that over Antarctica. The holes form over both polar regions for about six to eight weeks at a time. It takes several weeks of extremely cold (–50°C to –80°C) and stable temperatures to trigger the chemical reaction needed to produce the holes. Only in the polar regions can those conditions be found.

Depletion of the ozone layer could have serious effects on human health and the environment. Although much less severe than the antarctic ozone hole, the presence of an ozone hole in the Arctic, drifting about over populated areas, could pose a real health threat to northern peoples.

❄ Canada's current plan is to phase out all ozone-depleting substances as soon as possible, but no later than December 31, 1995, for CFCs and December 31, 1994, for halons.

Every one-percent decrease in ozone concentration could increase the amount of ultraviolet radiation by two percent. That could lead to nearly 50,000 new cases of skin cancer throughout Canada every year, including deadly melanoma. Other dangers include: accelerated skin and eye aging; acute sunburn; cataracts; suppression of the immune system, allowing tumours to grow; and decreased resistance to infectious diseases. Ozone depletion could also kill off plant and aquatic life, disrupt fish production, and endanger the world's major food crops.

Unfortunately, that is not the end of the story. CFCs are greenhouse gases. Like carbon dioxide, methane, water vapor and nitrous oxide, they trap infrared heat waves from the earth, intensifying the warming effect. Although CFCs are much less abundant than the other greenhouse gases, they are 10,000 times more efficient at warming up the atmosphere. If the atmosphere's temperature warms

---

BEING SUN SMART

- Don't use products with ozone-depleting chlorofluorocarbons (CFCs).
- Avoid the sun between 10 a.m. and 3 p.m. when UV intensity is highest.
- Wear a hat, long-sleeved clothing and UV-rated sunglasses outdoors.
- Wear a sunscreen with a Sun Protection Factor (SPF) rating of 15 or more.
- Apply the sunscreen a half-hour before you go outside, and reapply it after swimming or sports activities.

too much, major shifts in climate and weather patterns can be expected.

In spite of the possibility of thinning ozone layers elsewhere, and the realization that even with a total phasing out of ozone-destroying chemicals the situation will get worse before it gets better, there are some small but hopeful signs that the problem is being addressed. Industry is developing "safe" substitutes for CFCs. Politicians are taking the threat seriously and are acting to ban production and use of ozone-destroying chemicals. Canadian scientists are monitoring our ozone layer. And consumers are speaking out with the result that more egg cartons and hamburger containers are being made of cardboard again, safer propellants for aerosols are being used, and refrigerator-cooling gases are being recycled.

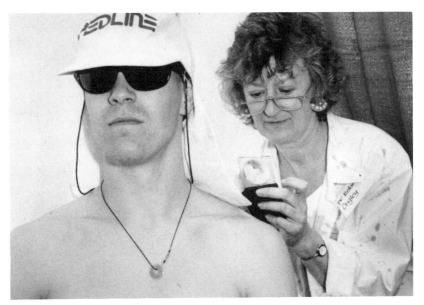

A skin cancer testing tent was set up at English Bay, Vancouver, in 1993. LES BAZSO/VANCOUVER PROVINCE

CANADIAN
METEOROLOGICAL
MOMENTS

THE DAY NIAGARA FALLS RAN DRY

ON THE NIGHT OF MARCH 29, 1848, THE UNTHINK-able happened. The mighty Niagara Falls eased to a trickle and then fell silent for 30 puzzling hours. It was the only time in recorded history that this wonder of the world had been stilled. So incredible was the event that three decades later eyewitnesses were still being asked to sign declarations swearing that they were there when "the Falls of Niagara ran dry."

Residents first realized that something was wrong when they were awakened by an overpowering, eerie silence. Inspection of the river by torches revealed only a few puddles of water in the river bed. The next morning some 5,000 sightseers from as far away as Hamilton and Buffalo jammed the roads to Niagara Falls and converged on the river bank to see the phenomenon. The American falls had slowed to a dribble, the British Channel was drying fast, and the thundering Canadian Horseshoe Falls were stilled. Upstream at Chippewa, the Welland River was reduced to a mere stream. Above the falls, water wheels at flour mills and factories stopped turning as the river level dropped.

❋ The American Falls was reduced to a mere trickle as ice dams cut off the flow of water in 1883, 1896, 1904, 1909, 1936 and 1947.

For some, the event was an interesting curiosity. Peering down from the bank, they saw long stretches of drying mud, exposed boulders and chains of black puddles. Fish and turtles lay floundering in crevices. While thousands stood in dis-belief, a few daredevils explored recesses and cavities at the bottom of the dry river gorge never before visible. They picked up bayonets, muskets, swords, gun barrels, tomahawks and other relics of the War of 1812. Others took the historic opportunity to cross the river above and below the falls — on foot, on horseback, or by horse and buggy. A squadron of United States cavalry troopers enjoyed the novelty of a ride down the river bed, while some young entrepreneurs parked a cart just above the brink of the Canadian Falls and retrieved huge pine timbers measuring 12 to 18 metres long. Years later, owners of furniture made from those once-submerged timbers delighted in recalling how the wood was obtained.

❄ On January 9, 1889, the Niagara Suspension Bridge, located just above the Falls, was blown down during a storm described in the press as "one of the greatest storms that has ever passed over any part of Canada."

Below the falls, the dry river course provided an opportunity to blast out the rocks that had scraped the keel of the *Maid of the Mist* since its launch in 1846. As one account stated, "The canyon of the river reverberated to constant blasting as the rocks were blown to pieces and removed with the same ease as if they had been on dry land."

For superstitious people the unusual silence and unexplained phenomenon was a portent of divine wrath or impending doom. As the day wore on, fear and anxiety spread. Thousands attended special church services on both sides of the border. Native people in the area shared in the belief that some disaster was about to happen.

Tension grew until the night of March 31, when a low growl from upstream announced the return of the waters. Suddenly, a wall of water surged down the river bed and over the falls. The deluge quickly covered the massive boulders at the base of the falls and restored the ever-present Niagara spray. Relieved residents relaxed and returned home to sleep again to the rumble and boom of the falls.

The cause of the stoppage, it was discovered later, was an ice jam that had formed on Lake Erie near Buffalo. In an average winter, Lake Erie is almost completely ice-covered. Normally, by the end of March the lake is clear except in the eastern basin near Buffalo where prevailing winds and water currents concentrate drifting ice. Westerly winds blowing down nearly 400 kilometres of open water break the ice into mammoth chunks and remould it into ridges and rafted ice. The thawing process accelerates in late March, especially on sunny days and under the flow of warm, moist, southerly air.

Contrary to published reports, the winter of 1847–48 was not intensely cold and Lake Erie's ice cover was not thicker than the usual 10 to 60 centimetres. In fact, that particular winter was about two degrees milder than usual, although the first half of March was unseasonably cold. In late March, several days of stiff easterly winds drove Erie's pack ice up the lake. But on March 29, the winds suddenly reversed direction, coming out of the southwest and west and propelling the vast ice field back down the lake. The ice was melting rapidly as afternoon temperatures went to 7°C under clear skies. The combined force of wind, waves and lake currents jammed hundreds of thousands of tonnes of ice into a solid dam at the neck of the lake and the river entrance between Fort Erie and Buffalo. Eventually, the ice cut off the water's flow and the basin downstream gradually dried out. The ice dam, however, was under constant assault. The weather continued balmy and nighttime temperatures stayed above freezing. On March 31, the temperature rose

❄ On January 27, 1938, the Honeymoon Bridge at Niagara Falls collapsed after a massive ice jam pushed it off its abutments. The ice, which piled up in the river after a storm on Lake Erie, also destroyed the *Maid of the Mist* docks and damaged a power plant.

to 16°C, the winds continued to shift and strengthen, and that night the Niagara ice wedge dislodged, restoring the river flow.

Will Niagara Falls ever run dry again? Probably not, at least not on its own accord. Since 1964, an ice boom has been positioned at the head of the Niagara River every winter to prevent the formation of ice blockages and safeguard hydroelectric installations.

The falls have been turned off, though. For seven months in 1969, the United States Army Corps of Engineers diverted the river to permit repairs to the eroding face of the American Falls. On six other recorded occasions, the American Falls have frozen over completely. February 1947 was especially cold and the channel on the north side of Goat Island, which separates the two falls, became completely blocked with large masses of ice. But not the Canadian Horseshoe Falls. With 10 times the volume of the American Falls, only once has its mighty roar been stilled — on that memorable March night in 1848.

REMEMBERING OUR LONGEST, HOTTEST HEAT WAVE

AT MIDALE, SASKATCHEWAN, ON JULY 5, 1936, farmer Samuel Molberg's thermometer registered 111°F (43.9°C). Already the heat wave was two days old. For a week newspaper headlines reported triple-figure temperatures (in Fahrenheit) and a soaring death count. From the Rockies to the Ottawa River, Canada

A snow fence is used to keep drifting soil off a highway near Estevan, Saskatchewan, during the drought years of the 1930s. SASKATCHEWAN ARCHIVES BOARD

simmered and baked during the most intense and extensive heat wave on record. It was the climax to the dustbowl era. Temperatures soared as high as 44.4°C (112°F) and, combined with extreme drought, produced huge economic losses — ruined crops, dead livestock, burned forests and buckled highways. But most of all, the '36 heat wave is remembered as a killer — 780 Canadians died.

❄ The hottest place in the world, with an average annual temperature in the shade of 34.4°C, is Dalol, Ethiopia, near the southern end of the Red Sea.

A heat wave is defined as a period of three or more consecutive days with temperatures of 32°C or higher. High humidities are not a requisite, yet most heat waves are oppressively humid. By these criteria, St. John's and Vancouver have never experienced a heat wave, and Victoria has had only one, lasting four days in 1941.

The frequency of hot spells increases inland. Periods of up to five successive hot days have been recorded in every province except Prince Edward Island and Newfoundland. The British Columbia interior usually records the most protracted heat waves — as long as 30 days. Across the southern Prairies and in southern Ontario, hot spells can last 10 to 15 days.

❄ In 1917, Death Valley, California, suffered 43 consecutive days with maximum temperatures over 48.9°C. It is the only known place in the United States where night-time temperatures sometime remain above 37.8°C.

The most memorable heat waves occurred during the droughts and dust storms on the Prairies in the '30s. Other notable heat waves were in August 1944 in the Maritimes, August 1953 in Ontario, July 1963 in Quebec, and August 1981 in southern British Columbia.

The searing 1936 heat wave originated in the southwestern United States and was continent-wide. Heat records that were set in 16 states still stand. Shade temperatures reached 49.5°C in Kansas and the Dakotas. From May to September, the weather stayed torrid and dry. In Kansas City, the mercury soared to 37.8°C (100°F) or higher on 53 days. The human catastrophe was enormous: 4,768 Americans died.

The heat wave penetrated Canada during the first week of July. In southern Saskatchewan and Manitoba, the hottest period ran 13 days from the 5th to the 17th, and in Ontario the spell lasted eight days beginning over northwestern Ontario on the 7th and ending across the province on the 14th.

In Manitoba, temperatures reached 44.4°C at St.

Albans on the 11th and at Emerson on the 12th, the hottest days ever recorded in the province. In sweltering Winnipeg, temperatures exceeded 32°C on 13 consecutive days and peaked at 42.2°C on the 11th. That night it "cooled" to 28.3°C.

In Ontario, a new provincial record of 42.2°C was set at Atikokan on the 11th and 12th and repeated at Fort Frances on the 13th. At Toronto, the heat wave was the most intense ever recorded in observations going back nearly a century. A peak of 41.1°C was recorded on the 10th and the "highest low" occurred early on the morning of the 11th — 26.6°C.

❄ The world record for shade temperature is 58°C at two places — al'Aziziyah, Libya, on September 13, 1922 and at San Luis, Mexico, on August 11, 1933.

During the 1970s, about seven Canadians died each year from excessive summer heat or too much sun. Among the natural hazards, only lightning and extreme cold take a greater human toll. However, there is nothing in Canadian history to compare with the losses counted during the 1936 heat wave, when 376 males and 404 females died, most of them elderly or infants. A year earlier there were only 42 heat-related deaths. In July 1936, there were another 400 indirect casualties including several drownings. Ontario had the greatest number of deaths — nearly 600 persons — and in Toronto over 225 succumbed to the heat. Heat-related deaths in Manitoba exceeded 70.

The combination of heat and drought cost farmers millions of dollars. Parched pasture lands forced widespread sell-off of dairy herds, resulting in milk shortages. In the Niagara fruit belt, berries withered on their stems and apples shrivelled on the trees. Poultry, pigs and pets died. But, for farmers with irrigation, the drought meant increased incomes from sharply rising prices.

For most of July, forest fires consumed vast areas of tinder-dry bush, and the smell of smoke filled the air across northern and central Ontario and parts of the Prairies. As more than 200 fires blazed between Sudbury and Thunder Bay, transients were taken off trains and conscripted to battle the flames. Residents packed belongings, cached valuables in deep, cold holes and awaited the call to evacuate. So limited was the water supply in the north, several hotels forbade anyone from taking a shower or bath. All areas experienced water shortages and rationed supplies. Interestingly, hydro demand was reduced, unlike during modern heat waves when consumption suddenly escalates from the use of air conditioners.

❋ A large man can perspire as much as 19 litres of water a day.

The heat buckled highways and softened asphalt. Tarred roads had to be sanded to reduce skidding. Surface temperatures exceeded 65°C. Brick sidewalks and roadways heaved, steel bridge girders warped and heavy steel rail lines twisted.

Conditions seemed worse in big cities. Toronto gasped, sagged and limped as the weather got hotter and hotter. Air conditioning was largely unavailable and refrigeration was a luxury. Lake Ontario was like a mill pond; however, swimming along the north shore offered no relief with the water an unusually cold 8°C. Offshore winds had stripped away any warm surface waters, allowing an upwelling of cold water from below.

❋ June 1961 was a record hot, dry month on the Canadian Prairies. In Alberta and parts of Saskatchewan, it was the warmest June on record, with average temperatures exceeding those of all but the very warmest Julys. It was the driest June ever in Manitoba and parts of Saskatchewan. Across the four western provinces there was more bright sunshine recorded than during any other June on record.

The heat wave touched everyone and everything:

- Several horses pulling milk and bread wagons dropped dead.
- Apart from the air-conditioned ground floors at Eaton's and Simpsons, most retail stores were empty.
- Industry either closed down or started earlier shifts.
- Sales of ice cream and soft drinks went up 50 percent; beverage room business was down because it was too hot to walk for a beer, but beer deliveries were way up.
- Concerned relatives made long-distance calls, 50 percent above normal.
- Demand for lemons shot prices up from 25 cents a dozen to 50.
- Long lines queued in front of air-conditioned theatres left open at night and on Sunday.
- Deliveries of ice were up 80 percent and were permitted on Sunday.
- Police chose not to enforce bylaws prohibiting topless male bathing suits; at Queen's University in Kingston, however officials clamped down on male students wearing exposed suspenders.
- Shower-bath installations, refrigerators and fans were in great demand.
- Frying eggs on sidewalks was tried everywhere.
- Thousands of comfort-seeking residents crowded the waterfront, parks and cemeteries bringing with them rugs, mattresses and car seats for sleeping; others slept on verandas and on front lawns.
- Numerous laundry workers and store clerks collapsed.
- A huge influx of Americans came north seeking relief.

> ❄ Globally, the 1980s was the hottest decade in 130 years of observations; the seven warmest years on record have occurred since 1980 — 1990, 1988, 1991, 1987, 1983, 1989, 1981. Global temperatures have increased by about 0.3°C over the last thirty years. The average global temperature is almost 16°C, the highest since global measurements began in the late 19th century.

- Across Toronto, cellars were turned into temporary bedrooms, dining rooms and cool refuges.
- Tennis courts and golf courses were deserted.
- Those who could not purchase electric fans used vacuum cleaners to blow air.
- Newspaper advertisements featured tropical suits, cold-plate specials, ice-box specials, fruit salts and iced tea.
- Theatre marquees gave top billing to "cooled by refrigeration."
- Outdated hearses were put back into service, extra grave-diggers were hired and florists were short of flowers; obituary columns swelled to four to five times their usual length.

❄ The summer of 1949 was the warmest on record over most of southern Ontario. Temperatures averaged 23°C between Toronto and Windsor over the June, July and August period.

The following year, on July 5, 1937, Sam Molberg's thermometer read 113°F (45°C), making Midale the hottest place ever in Canada, a record that still stands. Fortunately, it was just one exceptionally hot day, and not the start of another heat wave.

HOW TO COOL DOWN ON HOT DAYS

- Do outdoor chores in the early morning.
- Drink cool juices and water, not alcoholic beverages.
- Wear loose-fitting clothes made of natural fibres — cottons and linens.
- Take time to sit in the shade to relax and lower your body temperature.
- Cool down by running cold water on your wrists or by holding a wet towel against your neck or forehead.
- Eat less. Avoid sweets and fatty foods, which tend to warm you up. Vegetables and fruits keep you cooler and replace the salts, potassium and water you lose when you perspire.

WHEN SNOWSTORMS BECOME BLIZZARDS

WINTER STORMS AND EXCESSIVE COLD CLAIM OVER 100 lives in Canada every year, more than the combined toll from hurricanes, tornadoes, floods, extreme heat and lightning. Blizzards are easily the most feared and perilous of all winter storms.

Almost everyone is inclined to call any personally inconvenient snowstorm a blizzard. However, according to Environment Canada, a blizzard must consist of below-freezing temperatures, winds at or above 40 kilometres per hour, falling and blowing snow that reduces visibility to less than a kilometre, and a duration of at least three hours.

Snow in a blizzard is usually fine and powdery. Sometimes people suffocate in blizzards, their lungs choked with "floury" snow. Often the amount of newly fallen snow is negligible. One unforgettable blizzard in southern Saskatchewan lasted four days in February 1978. Snowdrifts reached rooftops in Regina, yet only a trace of new snow fell. The city acted like an enormous snow fence, blocking and trapping blowing snow that had fallen on the prairies weeks earlier.

❄ Artificial snow takes a lot of water and effort. It takes 50,000 litres of water to cover a ski slope of ½ hectare with about three centimetres of snow.

The character of severe weather varies greatly from place to place, so Environment Canada uses different criteria for defining blizzards in different regions. Criteria for wind (at or above 40 kilometres per hour) and for visibility (below one kilometre in snow or blowing snow) are the same everywhere, but temperature and storm durations are as follows: in

A snowstorm in Victoria Plains, Saskatchewan,
buried a Trans-Continental train for five days in 1947.
CANADIAN NATIONAL

Atlantic Canada, –3°C and lasting three or more consecutive hours; Quebec, –17°C and six hours; Ontario, –8°C
and four hours; Manitoba and Saskatchewan, –10°C and
six hours; Alberta, 0°C and three hours; interior British
Columbia, –10°C and six hours; coastal British Columbia,
5°C and six hours; Yukon, –10°C and three hours; and
Northwest Territories, 0°C and six hours.

Blizzards are rare along the British Columbia coast;
over the past 35 years, Vancouver and Victoria have not
recorded a single hour with blizzard conditions. Alberta's
worst snowstorms occur in the early spring but seldom
reach blizzard status. The southern prairies, on the other
hand, are said to be the home of the blizzard and at least
one major blow takes place every winter. Tales abound of
pioneer farmers who perished midway between house and

barn, or of early explorers who strayed only a metre or two away from campsites and died. Even today, winter brings reports of residents "storm stayed," livestock frozen in a corner of a field or in snow-filled barns, and wildlife killed by exposure and starvation.

Blizzards are most frequent in southern Saskatchewan: Swift Current and Regina average more than 30 hours of blizzard weather a year. Most blizzards there last an average of 12 hours, although 48-hour whiteouts have been recorded. To the north, blizzards occur much less frequently. At Saskatoon, blizzard hours average six a year but only once in four years does an "official" six-hour winter blow materialize.

The most memorable blizzard happened in February 1947. For 10 days all highways into Regina were blocked with snow. Streets in every southern Saskatchewan town were also blocked, and supplies of fuel, food and feed ran dangerously low. Outside Moose Jaw, a farmer cut a hole in his barn roof; it was the only way he could get in to milk his cows.

> ❄ Shovelling snow can be a strenuous experience. Forty centimetres of heavy, wet snow on a driveway measuring 15 by 4 metres weighs more than 12 tonnes!

Blizzards and drifting snow are a hazard on the open prairie of southern Manitoba, but less so in the parkland and forests where the force of the wind is broken. Winnipeg experiences blizzard conditions about 12 hours a year, yet seldom for the six-hour duration that defines a blizzard in that region. One of its worst storms occurred on November 8–9, 1986, when 35 centimetres of snow fell. Winds gusting to 90 kilometres per hour reduced visibility to zero and formed huge snowdrifts. Travel was impossible except by military vehicle, snowmobile and snowplow. Snow removal costs approached $3 million, and it took a week to get the city back to normal. The storm was similar to the March 1966

AVERAGE NUMBER OF BLIZZARD EVENTS/HOURS EACH WINTER

| | EVENTS | | HOURS | |
| | Based on | | Based on | |
	Regional Criteria	Alberta Criteria*	Regional Criteria	Alberta Criteria*
St. John's	3	6	24	47
Moncton	2	4	17	31
Montreal	<1	1	1	11
Ottawa	<1	1	1	5
Winnipeg	<1	2	12	18
Regina	2	5	31	37
Edmonton	<1		3	
Vancouver	0	0	0	0
Yellowknife	<1	1	4	4
Iqaluit	7	12	103	103

* Wind speed above 40 km/h, temperature below 0°C, visibility under 1 km in snow or blowing snow, and duration of three consecutive hours or more.

Based on 35 years of records 1953–87.

blizzard (36 centimetres of snow) but was exceeded by one in March 1935 (52 centimetres of snow).

The definition of a blizzard is more exacting in Ontario and Quebec. Consequently, official blizzards are rare — fewer than one a year in Ottawa and Montreal. However, blizzards are frequent in Atlantic Canada. Based on Atlantic blizzard criteria, Newfoundland, Prince Edward Island and New Brunswick are the most blizzard-ridden eastern provinces, experiencing two to three blizzards and between 15 and 25 blizzard-hours a year.

Perhaps surprisingly, blizzards are rare in the Yukon and the western Northwest Territories. Whitehorse has had only one blizzard in 35 years, and Yellowknife averages less than one major blizzard, or about four blizzard hours a winter. In the eastern Arctic, winds are stronger and blowing snow is more frequent. Iqaluit (formerly Frobisher Bay) averages seven blizzards and 103 blizzard-hours a year.

Blizzards are often associated with a wave of cold arctic air surging southward and bringing snow, rapidly falling temperatures and strong winds. Nicknamed "the norther," these storms move swiftly and are usually followed by another blow in a few days. Blizzards may also accompany strong low-pressure disturbances. When these lows move into Canada, frigid arctic air swings southward behind them. With strong winds, the chances are that even in the absence of falling snow, enough of it is whipped up off the ground to reduce visibility to near zero. One of the worst dangers for humans and other creatures in these whiteout conditions is getting lost.

The origin of the word *blizzard* is uncertain, but it is probably from English dialect sources. During the 1800s, the word was used in the United States to mean a severe blow, a cannon shot, or a volley of musketry. In 1835, Davy Crockett wrote about taking a blizzard (shot) at a deer and speaking a blizzard (a squelching retort or blast) during a dinner speech. In the English Midlands, *blizzer* referred to a severe storm of wind and snow, hail, rain, or dust. Blizzard was first used in North America in 1836 to refer to a sudden snowstorm. Today the word means a severe snowstorm in nearly every English-speaking country.

❄ About 36 percent of Canada's yearly precipitation occurs as snow, most of which covers the gound for several months before melting. By comparison, only 5 percent of the earth's precipitation falls as snow.

CANADA'S TEN WORST BLIZZARDS

- **Regina, January 30, 1947.** A blizzard raged for 10 days. The railway called it the worst storm in Canadian rail history — one train was buried in a snowdrift one kilometre long and eight metres deep.
- **Newfoundland, February 16, 1959.** "The worst ever" snowstorm claimed six lives, left 70,000 without services, and blocked roads with five-metre drifts.
- **Winnipeg, March 4, 1966.** A storm brought 36 centimetres of snow and 120-kilometre-per-hour winds, paralysing the city for two days.
- **Montreal, March 4, 1971.** The city's worst storm dumped 47 centimetres of snow. Winds of 110 kilometres per hour produced huge drifts. Electricity was cut for two to seven days.
- **Niagara Peninsula, January 28, 1977.** The start of a three-day storm described as the worst winter storm in memory.
- **London, December 9, 1977.** A fierce winter blow over three days left 100 centimetres of snow. Huge drifts blocked all roads. Emergency forces were brought into the city.
- **Iqaluit, Northwest Territories, February 8, 1979.** A –40°C temperature and 100-kilometre-per-hour winds with snow kept residents indoors for 10 days.
- **Prince Edward Island, February 22, 1982.** Islanders were marooned for five days in a crippling blizzard. Winds of 80 kilometres per hour whipped a 60-centimetre snowfall into seven-metre drifts.
- **Southern Alberta, May 14, 1986.** A two-day storm was described as the worst spring storm in Alberta. Knee-deep snow and 80-kilometre-per-hour winds left dozens of communities without services.
- **Winnipeg, November 7, 1986.** A major storm dumped 30 centimetres of snow on the city. Winds gusting to 90 kilometres per hour produced severe blowing snow and zero visibility across southern Manitoba. Clean-up costs approached $3 million.

Aftermath of an 1898 Hamilton, Ontario freezing rain storm. EDWIN A. GAVILLER/NATIONAL ARCHIVES OF CANADA/C-35838

WINTER'S CRUEL FAIRYLAND OF ICE

PICTURE WINTER'S MOST ENCHANTING SCENE: A GLIT-tering, sunny landscape encrusted with an icy glaze applied by a night of freezing rain.

For most, an ice storm is the loveliest yet most destructive form of winter weather. Its price is often blackouts and disrupted telephone service, slippery streets made impassable to vehicles and pedestrians,

78

broken tree limbs and downed utility lines, sidewalks covered with a slick of black ice, and roofs rendered unsafe by heavy ice loading. Often more crippling than a snowstorm, an ice storm's legacy of havoc and disruption may remain for days or even weeks. One of the most memorable such storms struck eastern Ontario and southwestern Quebec on Christmas Eve in 1986. After 14 hours of freezing rain, one Ottawa home in four was left without electricity; on Christmas Day, many residents cooked their turkeys on propane barbecues or had dinner with more fortunate friends or relatives.

Forecasting the advent and amount of freezing precipitation in its many forms — sleet, glaze, ice pellets, rime, freezing rain and freezing drizzle — is always a challenge for the meteorologist. While the temperature hovers around freezing, the odds for rain, freezing rain, snow, ice pellets or some congealed mixture of all four are about even. A one-degree shift to either side of freezing can determine whether liquid or frozen precipitation falls.

For freezing precipitation, there must be a layer of warm air aloft and a deep layer of subzero surface air below. As snowflakes fall through the warmer inversion layer, they melt into raindrops. When they fall through the subzero layer, the drops freeze and reach the ground as frozen raindrops, referred to by forecasters as ice pellets in Canada and sleet in the United States. These more-or-less clear particles of ice have a diameter of about five millimetres, only slightly larger than the raindrops from which they formed. The pellets bounce when striking the ground and produce a tapping sound when they hit glass or metal. Ice pellets generally do not cling to wires or exposed surfaces unless accompanied by rain or wet snow.

❄ Ice is much smoother near the freezing point than at lower temperatures. At −18°C, a car can stop on glaze in half the distance it needs at −1°C.

❄ Ice storms are sometimes incorrectly referred to as sleet storms. The term *sleet* is not used by Environment Canada. Instead, the term *ice pellets* is used to describe frozen raindrops or pellets of snow encased in a thin layer of ice. They are spherical or irregular shapes with a diameter of 5 millimetres or less. Pellets do not stick to trees and wires, but may, if sufficiently deep, cause hazardous driving conditions. In some parts of the United States, *sleet* is used to describe precipitation in the form of a mixture of rain and snow.

Sometimes the cold surface layer is too shallow or not cold enough to freeze the raindrops completely as they fall. In this case, the drops reach the surface as a supercooled liquid (water droplets at a temperature below 0°C) or as a mixture of liquid and ice. Upon striking a cold object, such as the pavement, building walls or cars, they spread out and freeze almost immediately, forming a smooth, thin veneer of ice. This is called freezing rain, or glaze. If the drops are tiny (less than 0.5 millimetres in diameter), the precipitation is called freezing drizzle. An ice glaze contains no air bubbles and looks as smooth and clear as glass — and sticks tenaciously to the object it coats.

In many storms there is actually an organized evolution of precipitation types. If the precipitation begins as snow, it changes to a mixture of snow and ice pellets; then snow, ice pellets and freezing rain; then ice pellets and freezing rain; and finally to freezing rain alone.

Rime, a type of hoar frost, is another form of icing that adheres to exposed surfaces such as aircraft wings, large transmission towers and telephone poles. When an aircraft flies through a cloud, tiny supercooled water droplets may strike its surface and freeze instantly before they have time to spread. Thus rime ice is formed. The frozen droplets trap air between them, giving the rime a milky, feathery appearance, much like that of freezer crystals. It is lighter, softer, rougher and less transparent than glaze. Sometimes, a mixture of rime and glaze forms on aircraft surfaces.

FREEZING PRECIPITATION GLOSSARY

- **Diamond dust.** At very cold temperatures, some water droplets in the air may freeze. These tiny ice crystals or needles fall very slowly, glittering in the sunshine like diamond dust.
- **Glaze ice.** This type of ice is generally clear, smooth, hard and highly adhesive.
- **Rime ice.** It is opaque and milky, contains many air bubbles, and has moderate adhesive qualities.
- **Hoar frost.** Hoar frost has interlocking white and feathery ice crystals, with a low adhesive quality.

Rime may form when fog or mist is present as well.

Wet snow may also stick to wires and cables and freeze into rime. Sometimes the buildup of wet snow on the windward side of the wire will rotate the line, offering a new surface for more snow to cling to. In time, the wire may twist completely so that when the encircling wet snow eventually freezes into rime, the line may well snap under the added weight.

The severity of ice storms depends largely on the amount of ice accumulation, the duration of the storm, and the location and extent of the area affected. One of the worst ice storms ever in Newfoundland struck St. John's on the evening of April 11, 1984. Jackets of ice up to 15 centimetres thick formed on overhead wires. The interruption of power left 200,000 people in the Avalon Peninsula without heat and light for days, causing a run on kerosene heaters. In March 1958, St. John's experienced 43 hours of continuous freezing rain, with all the resultant chaos.

Atlantic Canada is especially prone to ice storms, and ice sheaths as thick as 40 centimetres have coated towers and guy wires. Sometimes wet snow falling during or after the freezing rain increases the accretion to such an enormous weight that utility poles topple and transmission towers bend under their icy load.

One of the longest-lasting ice storms occurred in southern Ontario in January 1968 — three days, off and on, of freezing rain and wet snow. The storm was one of the worst on record in the province. Live hydro wires buried under the snow added a dimension of real danger.

Strong winds aid and abet the disruption and damage. Stress on overhead wires may be increased when the wind blows at right angles to the lines, causing galloping waves that may snap insulators, supports and wires. The Montreal area suffered through one of the most destructive ice storms in Canadian history on February 25, 1961. Wires heavily loaded with five centimetres of ice snapped in winds gusting to 120 kilometres per hour, leaving some areas of the city without electricity for a week.

❄ An average evergreen tree, 15 metres high with a spread of 6 metres, weighs 4,500 kilograms when covered with glaze from a freezing rainstorm.

Freezing precipitation is, in fact, a hazard in all parts of Canada, although years may pass without any occurrences in the Yukon and coastal British Columbia. Freezing rain falls on average less than five hours a year in the inland British Columbia valleys. One of the most notorious places for icing was Old Glory Mountain, a weather station at 2,347 metres above sea level near Castlegar, British Columbia. The weather station operated from 1944 to 1967, when it burned down. Because of its elevation, most of the ice coating at Old Glory was rime icing from clouds rather than accretions from freezing precipitation.

The prairies generally have one or two severe ice storms a year. Winnipeg's most memorable major glazing happened on March 6, 1983. Thick ice on the runways

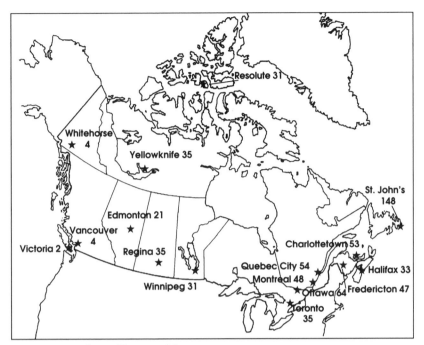

Average number of hours of freezing precipitation a year.

at Winnipeg International Airport forced its closure for two days, and several large television towers collapsed under the weight of ice. Storm clean-up costs exceeded $2 million.

Winter freezing precipitation, however, is most prevalent across southeastern Canada from Ontario to Newfoundland. Icing reaches its maximum intensity and duration in Newfoundland where freezing rain storms occur from December through April. The riskiest months for freezing rain are November and December in the West, November through February on the Prairies, December through March in the southern regions of Ontario and Quebec, and in the Maritimes. Winter is too cold for freezing precipitation in the High Arctic; up there, it falls in the summer.

WINTER STORM SAFETY TIPS

- Winterise your car before the storm season begins.
- Put together a winter storm kit for your car that includes a flashlight, booster cables, a warning light or road flares, a shovel, blankets, candle and matches, and a first-aid kit.
- Listen to the latest weather reports and heed storm warnings before venturing out.
- Dress to suit the weather conditions.
- If trapped in a blizzard on the road, try to stay in your vehicle. Run the motor and heater sparingly to avoid a buildup of deadly carbon monoxide. If you must go out to push or dig, avoid exposure and overexertion caused by frantic shovelling.
- In your home have a good supply of heating fuel, emergency food, batteries and prescription drugs.
- If you have a farm, ensure animals are stabled and have plenty of food and water.

The effects of ice storms are well known to most Canadians — widespread power outages, closed schools and businesses, cancelled deliveries, disrupted mail and emergency services, and collapsed buildings, signs and antennae. Costs are enormous as work crews struggle to restore services and clean up physical damage. Power outages mean milking machines must sit idle in rural districts, and everywhere tonnes of freezer food begin thawing. But the costs of frustration, personal inconvenience, discomfort and absenteeism are seldom tallied.

✳ Tradition has it that a century or more ago, the forecast was for "plain rain." Instead, a freeze occurred. Someone sardonically noted that the expected thaw had a "silvery" look to it, hence the name "silver thaw."

The real victims of ice storms are birds and small animals, which can no longer reach their food supplies, and trees. A twig in an average storm may have to bear ice weighing six times its own weight. The loss of branches can retard tree growth for years after a major ice storm.

Most ice storms come silently in the night. In the morning, the sunlight glints off ice-coated surfaces, dazzling us for a while until the full extent of the storm's passing becomes apparent.

IT NEVER RAINS BUT IT POURS

W HETHER WE LIKE IT OR NOT, CANADA IS DRENCHED, blanketed and pelted by 5.5 trillion tonnes of rain, snow and hail each year. That adds up to enough moisture to keep the Niagara River flowing for 30 years. However, when averaged out and shared across the land, albeit unevenly, it translates into a less intimidating 535 millimetres of annual precipitation.

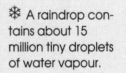

❊ A raindrop contains about 15 million tiny droplets of water vapour.

For people living in such northerly places as Eureka on Ellesmere Island, an overabundance of precipitation is not a concern. A year's rain and snow usually amounts to a scant 64 millimetres — a mere drop in the bucket compared to the annual 6,655-millimetre deluge at Henderson Lake on the west coast of Vancouver Island.

The Pacific Coast is the country's wettest region, with rainfalls exceeding 3,000 millimetres annually over large areas. Yet less than 100 kilometres to the east, across the Coast Mountains, lies a sagebrush-dotted semi-desert in the Fraser River valley that is one of Canada's driest areas.

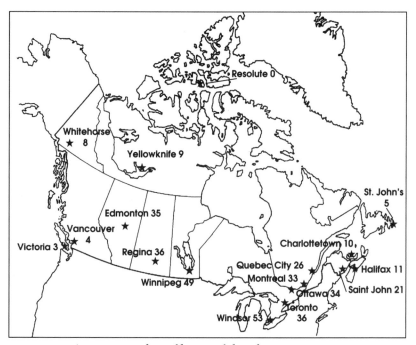

Average number of hours of thunderstorm activity a year.

There the average annual precipitation is 400 millimetres, with some localities receiving less than 250 millimetres.

Across the Prairies the annual precipitation ranges from 350 millimetres to 500 millimetres, increasing at a rate of about 40 millimetres for every 100 kilometres to the east. It rises from 500 millimetres a year at Winnipeg to 1,500 millimetres at Halifax. Eastern Canada usually has ample and reliable quantities of rain and snow. Ontario and Quebec have no special wet or dry seasons, whereas the end of the year is the wettest time for the Atlantic Coast. In the North, the arctic desert has a meagre 100 to 200 millimetres of rainfall and even less snowfall.

The amount of rain or snow that reaches the ground can vary dramatically on any given day, even over short distances. Many people have experienced a near-deluge of

Flooding from a July 19 and 20, 1989 thunderstorm over Essex County, Ontario. WINDSOR STAR PHOTO

rain in their backyard, while at the same time, their front yard or their neighbour's remains quite dry. Intense rainfalls may occur in Canada under a variety of meteorological situations:

• Thunderstorms may produce short bursts of rain over small areas (less than 100 square kilometres) anywhere in southern Canada. Enormous rainfall amounts of 50 to 80 millimetres are not uncommon from a single thunderstorm, especially one that remains stationary for one or two hours or moves very slowly. Occasionally, such a storm gives rise to a flash flood — a sudden rush of water channelled into a narrow gulley, valley or watercourse, often with devastating results.

• Storm systems may stall along the Pacific Coast and pump moist air up the slopes of the adjacent mountains

> ❄ If all the water in the world — liquid, frozen and vapour — were poured upon Canada, it would cover the land surface to a depth of 137 kilometres.

resulting in prolonged periods of heavy rain. What these storms lack in rainfall intensity, they make up in duration. Such a storm can last for several days, and in doing so pour 300 millimetres or more of rain over several thousand square kilometres.

• Dying tropical storms or hurricanes may trigger downpours. Some of Eastern Canada's worst floods have resulted from the prolonged and drenching rains brought by dissipating Atlantic hurricanes.

Occasionally, these intense storms position themselves over a region, soaking one unfortunate area while leaving nearby locations dry. On May 30, 1961, one such storm struck the hamlet of Buffalo Gap, Saskatchewan, about 150 kilometres south of Regina near the United States border. In less than an hour, the monstrous thunderstorm poured more than 250 millimetres of rain on the town, which, until then, had been enduring one of the worst droughts in prairie history.

There were no official weather service measurements of the storm's rainfall since rain gauges were swept away by the flood waters. Officials from the Prairie Farm Rehabilitation Administration in Regina sent a team of engineers and meteorological technicians to investigate the magnitude of the rainfall and to obtain estimates of peak run-off rates. A "bucket survey," using garbage cans, battery jars, old crocks, tin cans, and wheelbarrows, turned up 21 usable estimates of the storm rainfall. More than 30 individuals — residents, highway officials, grain company agents,

> ❄ In an average year, approximately 5,600 umbrellas are lost on transit vehicles in Toronto; 25,200 in London, England.

farmers and their wives, and municipal workers — were interviewed. Many people mentioned the unusual sky colours just before the rains came: black clouds with greenish, pinkish and brownish hues. Most, however, remembered the rolling, churning and folding of the storm clouds, and the appearance of a huge dust cloud moving from the south, just ahead of the main storm from the southwest.

Generally, rainfall totals exceeded 75 millimetres within 100 kilometres of Buffalo Gap, but at the storm centre, authorities concluded that the peak rainfall exceeded 250 millimetres.

Hail accompanied the rainstorm, first as hailstones the size of peas, then larger, about the size of grapes, and finally the size of pullet eggs. Considerable damage resulted. The south and west sides of walls were stripped clean of paint, leaving buildings two-toned. The ground looked as if there had been a winter blizzard, and piles of hailstones were deposited four metres deep on the south side of grain elevators. Ten days later, hailstones still lay under rubble.

Run-off rates were spectacular, and the evidence was engraved on the prairie landscape — rills and gullies were stripped of topsoil and greenery. Even bark was stripped from trees. The surging waters of Big Beaver Creek carried away tree limbs, fragments of buildings, bridge spans and any loose object that was buoyant. Frank Beler, a Saskatchewan Wheat Pool agent, reported that "pig pens (full and empty), gas barrels, outdoor

> ❄ McInnes Island, British Columbia, recorded 265 millimetres of rain in a six-hour period between 5 a.m. and 11 a.m. on January 26, 1984. This is a six-hour Canadian record. The record is appended with an E for "estimated" because of the possible addition of sea-spray in the gauge due to the strong winds and high waves prevalent at the time.

> ❄ The intensity of rain is classified as: light (if falling at less than 2.5 millimetres per hour); moderate (if falling between 2.6 and 7.5 millimetres per hour), and heavy (if falling at 7.6 millimetres per hour or more).

toilets, timbers, CPR ties, ladders, wooden sidewalks and telegraph poles went through town like sailboats." Just before the storm hit, he managed to close the grain elevator doors and windows and turn off the power. During the storm, he rescued his mother and emptied the rain gauge three times, despite being bombarded with hailstones the size of golf balls, which left him covered with black-and-blue marks.

Roads were made impassable for days; telephone and telegraph lines were downed; and long stretches of snow, farm and railway fences disappeared. Strong winds pushed an empty boxcar up a 50-metre grade and into mud up to its axles. Countless buildings tottered on their undermined foundations or were swept along with the debris in the rolling waters. Remarkably, there were no deaths and very few injuries; pets, chickens and other small farm animals were the only casualties.

Another thunderstorm lingered over the lower Great Lakes region for 20 hours in July 1989, soaking the southern half of Essex County in southwestern Ontario with a record rainfall. Triggered by a low-pressure system stalled over northern Ohio, the storm dumped one of the greatest amounts of rain recorded by an Environment Canada rain gauge in Eastern Canada. The 264 millimetres that fell on the town of Harrow surpassed any official 24-hour rainfall previously recorded

> ❄ The atmosphere contains nearly 13 billion litres of water.

east of Vancouver Island, and exceeded even Hurricane Hazel's highest 48-hour total in 1954 by 40 percent. Even more incredible was the estimated rainfall that fell west of Harrow at the storm's centre. An analysis from a dense network of commercial tube gauges and water buckets of every conceivable type revealed a storm rainfall of 442 millimetres in less than 19 hours.

❄ Ten millimetres of rainfall over a hectare of land weighs about 250 tonnes.

It was the rainstorm of the century. The torrential rains and severe flooding left the region in chaos, forcing at least 5,000 people from their homes and cottages, some of which were swept into Lake Erie. More than 85 percent of the homes in the southern half of Essex County suffered basement or yard flooding. Among the floating debris were freezers, mattresses, cars, carpeting, furniture, floor boards and those blue boxes used for collecting recyclable material. Huge chunks of pavement were washed away and power, water and telephone lines were cut, leaving thousands of residents and one hospital without essential services. Early on the morning of July 20, a train carrying toxic chemicals derailed near Kingsville, and several families had to be evacuated. Residents waded through hip-deep water in flooded streets and, later, spent days vacuuming murky water from their homes.

Much of the county's rich farmland was submerged. Losses in tomato crops, raspberries and winter wheat, in one of Canada's prime farming regions, exceeded $15 million. Total storm and flood losses approached $50 million, and Ontario declared parts of the county a disaster area.

❄ The amount of rain, snow and hail that falls to earth each year is equivalent to 380 million litres for every person in Canada. This is enough for each person to have 9,000 baths a day.

The highest Canadian precipitation amounts measured for periods from hours to years have been recorded at

CANADA'S WETTEST HOURS*

Province/ Territory	Millimetres	Location	Date
Alberta	63	Lethbridge	July 1, 1982
British Columbia	49	Bear Creek	October 29, 1966
Manitoba	96	Porcupine Mountain	August 28, 1966
Newfoundland	46	Gander	August 6, 1949
New Brunswick	55	Centreville	August 14, 1976
Northwest Territories	27	Yellowknife Airport	July 6, 1985
Nova Scotia	56	Shelburne	July 24, 1988
Ontario	87	Fergus	June 10, 1967
Prince Edward Island	43	Summerside	August 9, 1980
Quebec	84	Montreal McGill	July 14, 1987
Saskatchewan	82	Swift Current	June 14, 1964
Yukon	28	Fort Selkirk	July 23, 1969

* Maximum rainfall amounts in one hour as measured by tipping bucket rain gauges operated at Environment Canada weather stations (1900 to 1990).

Environment Canada weather reporting stations in British Columbia. Measurements are currently taken at nearly 2,500 locations across the country. Over the years more than 8,000 sites have been sampled for varying periods. The dubious distinction of the wettest day belongs to Ucluelet on the west coast of Vancouver Island. On October 6, 1967, 489 millimetres of rain fell, a Canadian record, but only one-quarter the amount that fell at the world's wettest place, Cilaos on La Réunion Island in the Indian Ocean, which recorded 1,870 millimetres on March 15–16, 1952.

CANADA'S WETTEST DAYS*

Province/ Territory	Millimetres	Location	Date
Alberta	213	Eckville South	June 1970
British Columbia	489	Ucluelet	October 1967
Manitoba	217	Riding Mountain Park	September 1975
New Brunswick	179	Alma	April 1962
Newfoundland	173	St. John's	August 1876
Northwest Territories	91	Ennadai Lake	September 1972
Nova Scotia	239	Halifax	September 1942
Ontario	264	Harrow	July 1989
Prince Edward Island	164	Charlottetown	September 1942
Quebec	172	Barrage des Quinze	August 1932
Saskatchewan	179	Willmar	July 1984
Yukon	91	Quiet Lake	July 1972

* Maximum rainfall during a 24-hour period measured by gauges operated at Environment Canada weather stations. Estimates from non-official gauges (as at Buffalo Gap) have not been included in this table.

Canada's wettest hour, between 4:30 and 5:30 p.m. at Buffalo Gap when 250 millimetres fell in 1961, compares well with the world's wettest hour at the Kilauea sugar plantation, Kauai, Hawaii, and its 305 millimetres.

The accompanying table compares the wettest days on record in Canada.

FOLKLORE
AND MYTHS

"RED SKY AT NIGHT" AND OTHER WEATHER WHIMSY

I T IS ALMOST HERESY FOR SOMEONE FROM ENVIRONMENT Canada to admit to believing, let alone enjoying, as I do, those whimsical maxims, anecdotes and rhyming superstitions about the weather. Some sayings have survived for centuries, and a few have stood the test of scientific scrutiny even though they were developed without instruments or knowledge about the causes of weather.

The cleverest couplets are usually the most absurd. Here are two:

Onion skins very thin,
Mild winter's coming in.
Onion skins thick and tough,
Coming winter cold and rough.

When a cow tries to scratch its ear,
It means a shower is very near.
When it thumps its ribs with its tail,
Look out for thunder, lightning and hail.

> ❄ Whichever way a cat's rear-end is turned up when it licks itself, that's the way the wind is going to blow. (King's County, Nova Scotia)

Long before meteorologists discovered fronts, jet streams and polar vortices, there were shepherds and sailors, hunters and gatherers — people whose lives and livelihoods depended on the weather — who relied on nature to warn of coming storms or to give clues about the severity or mildness of the approaching season. They showed a keen sense of observation and quickly connected changes in nature with rhythms or patterns of weather. Farmers watched cloud movement and the sky colour to know when to sow and reap. Mariners noted wind shifts and watched wave motions for signs of change. Hunters studied the behaviour of insects and animals and, through repeated observation, learned to foretell the weather. They recalled what they saw in the form of short sayings, often embodied in rhyme for ease of memory. Many of these saws have persisted because they work and have became part of our folklore.

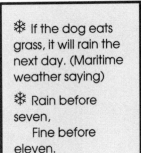

❄ If the dog eats grass, it will rain the next day. (Maritime weather saying)

❄ Rain before seven,
    Fine before eleven.

There are generally three classes of climatological fact and fable: those that suggest monthly, seasonal or long-term change; those that involve weather on key dates or anniversaries; and those that prophesy daily weather change.

Weatherlore attempting to predict for long periods is entirely without any physical basis. Among some of the more outlandish ones are:

The longer a porcupine's quills in the fall, the snowier it will be.

A warm January brings a wet spring.

Bushy tails on squirrels mean a cold winter is coming.

A cold winter means a hot summer.

The wider the brown bands on woolly bear caterpillars' backs, the colder will be the coming winter.

❄ When a horse yawns, it is a sign of soft (fine) weather. (King's County, Nova Scotia)

97

If squirrels gather more nuts than normal, it will be cold.

If blue jays appear happy in the fields after the harvest, it will be a mild winter.

When muskrats build their houses early, a tough winter will follow.

Heavy fur on beavers, muskrats, dogs and other animals indicates the approach of a severe winter.

Proverbs that connect weather events on one special date with conditions for particular days, months or seasons ahead are generally without foundation. It is only by coincidence that the weather may turn out as the proverb suggests. St. Swithin's Day (July 15) is one of the oldest key dates, going back to A.D. 862.

> ❄ If half of the breast bone of a cooked turkey is brown and half is white, then winter will be cold at first and will then warm up in January or February. (King's County, Nova Scotia)

St. Swithin's Day if ye do rain,
For forty days it will remain;
St. Swithin's Day an ye be fair,
For forty days 'twill rain nae mair.

And of course there is February 2.

If Groundhog Day be fair and bright,
Winter will have another flight,
But if Groundhog Day brings cloud and rain,
Winter is gone and won't come again.

Other sayings linked to a particular day are:

If it thunders on All Fools' Day, it brings good crops of corn and hay.

Rain at Easter gives slim fodder.

A rainy Easter means a good harvest.

❄ If the cats get restless and wrestle, there will be a storm. (Maritime weather saying)

Every March we hear "in like a lion, out like a lamb," and vice versa. Rube Hornstein, a popular meteorologist in the Maritimes, now retired, has proven that this saying is inaccurate for Halifax eight out of 10 times. In Toronto, it fares only a little better, being right three out of 10 times. However, it is nice to know that, generally, *April showers do bring May flowers.*

Most weatherlore relates to short-range weather conditions six to 24 hours ahead. Some are silly, illogical and quite outlandish; for example:

Thunder and lightning turn milk sour.

Lightning never strikes twice in the same place. (Tell that to the American forest ranger struck by lightning seven times.)

Kill a spider, it will rain within 24 hours.

When a dog howls at the moon, it is a sign of snow.

❄ Snow like meal,
   Snow a great deal.
   Snow like feathers,
   Softening weather.

If a rooster sits on a fence and crows early in the morning, it will rain.

It's too cold to snow.

> ❄ Whenever coyotes start yipping and howling together, the weather is going to change from good to bad. (Kelowna, British Columbia)

However, there are many short-term weather maxims that have survived the test of careful observation and scientific reasoning to become reliable guides to coming weather change. Those that seem to work and have a firm scientific basis are those pertaining to the condition of the atmosphere, the appearance of the sky, the character and movement of clouds, and the direction and force of the winds. Among the more reliable are:

A ring around the sun or moon,
Brings rain or snow upon you soon.

High, thin, ice crystal clouds (cirrus) — usually the fore-runners of unsettled wet weather — refract light from the sun and moon in a way that produces a halo.

The moon and the weather may change together,
But a change of the moon does not change the weather.

True, there is no connection between the phases of the moon and the weather.

If there is frost or dew, or morning fog,
No rain this day will you log.

On clear, cool, calm nights, ground moisture in the form of frost, dew or fog may form more readily because clouds are not present to interfere with ground cooling. Calm, clear nights are typical of high-pressure weather conditions and fine weather is likely to continue for at least the next day. Cloudy nights return heat lost from the ground so that dew or frost is not likely to form.

> When wind is in the east,
> 'Tis good for neither man or beast.

There is some truth to this saying in Canada, where storms to the south will likely produce an east wind while the air around the storm rotates in a counterclockwise direction. Not so in the southern hemisphere.

> Red sky at night, sailors (shepherds) delight,
> Red sky in morning, sailors (shepherds) take warning.

Versions of this jingle can be traced back to early Greek times. Being useful and largely truthful, it has survived centuries and seems to work well in Canada where weather patterns generally progress from west to east. Therefore, whatever is in the western, reddish sky tonight (fine dry weather for some distance) is likely to be overhead the next day. On the other hand, if the rising sun in the east produces a red sky, it means that fair weather has passed to the east and that wet, unsettled weather with thickening clouds cannot be far behind.

> ❋ When robins cry shriller, rain's coming in. (Salmo, British Columbia)

Insects, plants and animals are particularly sensitive to changes in the weather and have been the source of countless weather sayings over the ages. Some of the better-known are:

> Counting the number of cricket chirps in eight seconds and adding four will give the temperature within one degree Celsius.

The higher the temperature, the faster ants will move.

Insects are cold blooded, and their degree of activity is proportional to the temperature.

If the maple tree runs faster, it is going to rain.

Before rain, the atmospheric pressure usually falls. To equalize the pressure, the sap in trees begins to flow.

Bees stay close to their hive before rain.

Expect stormy weather when ants travel in lines and fair weather when they scatter.

Fish leap before a storm.

When quail are heard in the evening, one can expect fair weather the next day.

❄ Seagull, seagull,
sit on the sand,
    It's a sign of rain
when you're at
hand.

Flies and mosquitoes
Are biting and humming,
Swallows fly low
A rainstorm is coming.

Then, of course, there is our favourite aunt or uncle who can feel or smell a storm coming.

Aches and pain,
Coming rain.

Something about decreasing pressure causing tissue to expand a bit, sensitizing nerve cells and causing pain, is the basis for this one.

And there is an endless list of rain signs that many farmers swear by:

Cows huddle together or lie down in the pasture.

A pig scratches against a post.

Horses stand with their tails to the wind or roll over.

Chickens eat more.

The cat sits with his back to the fire.

The goose honks low (flies low).

Flowers smell sweeter.

Manure piles smell stronger.

The cock crows before going to bed.

> ❄ If you can't see Mount Baker, it's raining. If you can see it, it's a sign of rain. (New Westminster, British Columbia)

Now if these were true in any way, you'd expect rain almost every day.

WIND — BY MANY OTHER NAMES

MORE THAN ANY OTHER WEATHER ELEMENT, WIND HAS fascinated people throughout the ages. Our ancestors were all too familiar with wind's unpleasant effects — hot searing air, driving rain, drifting soil, blowing snow, chilling breezes, destructive gales. However, they were also well aware of winds that brought pleasure and comfort, pushed away ice, dissipated fog, helped move ships, and generated power.

In ancient times, winds were thought to be controlled by magic or by gods and goddesses: Wind gods were revered by the early Chinese and Egyptians; in Greece, the Tower of the Winds was erected to immortalize wind characteristics. In many cultures, the folklore was resplendent with imaginative references to wind. According to one native North American legend, the North Wind was a cruel and demanding monster who had to be humoured. Another legend told of a hunter who hunted the great bird whose beating wings caused the wind. He broke its wing. When the bird healed, its wing was smaller and could only produce a breeze.

❄ At a wind speed of 160 kilometres per hour, a person can lean forward on the wind with straight legs and touch the ground with his or her hand without falling over.

Our ancestors soon learned that changes in the wind often brought changes in the weather. It was said, "To read the wind correctly is to read the weather." From this understanding came countless sayings to forecast the weather:

The Devil is busy in a high wind.

No weather is ill,
If the wind be still.

Wind in the west,
Weather at its best.

A southerly wind with showers of rain,
Will bring the wind from the west again.

When wind comes before rain,
Soon you may make sail again.

The sharper the blast,
The sooner it's past.

If wind rises at night,
It will fall at daylight.

❄ Why are wind vanes traditionallly in the shape of a rooster? In the ninth century, Pope Nicholas I ordered that weather vanes in the form of a rooster be placed on all churches and abbeys as a reminder of the cock that crowed when Peter the Apostle denied Christ.

So important were the winds to early civilizations in different parts of the world, they were given names. Winds such as the chilling *bise* of Switzerland and northern France, the scorching, out-of-Africa *simoon* of the middle and southern Mediterranean regions, the dreaded *buran* of central Asia, the oppressive *berg* of coastal South Africa, the fierce *mistral* of France's lower Rhône Valley, the fickle *foehn* of the Alps, and the migraine-inducing *sharav* of Israel are fairly well known. Others, such as Hawaii's *kohilo* and the West African *cacimbo*, are enjoyed as refreshing, pleasant breezes.

Canada is home to the *chinook* (also called "rancher's friend" and "snow-eater") and to several other winds with special names — at least 70. An inordinate number are from marine-conscious Newfoundland, such as the *lun, dwye, strife, stun breeze* and *sheelagh* (but not the twister, which is a rolled cigarette in Newfoundland). Several others have an Indian origin; *keewatin* and *siwash*, for example.

Some Canadian-named winds reveal the direction of the blow (*in-wind, suete, nordet*), the coldness of the air (*cold maker, woolly whipper*), or the gentleness or fury of the wind (*airsome, dally*). Other names mimic wind

❄ When the wind is about 15 kilometres per hour, a flag flutters about one-third of the way out from a perpendicular staff. At about 30 kilometres per hour, a flag unfurls about two-thirds of the way, and at 50 kilometres per hour or more, a flag waves in full horizontal position.

sounds (*faffering*, *shuff*, *screecher*); suggest its effects on the land or people (*lamb-killer*, *cow storm*, *wreckhouse*); or indicate its geographic origin (*Yoho blow*, *Taku*, *Squamish*). Still others are merely exotic (*haboob*, *Sheila's brush*) or descriptive (*hog's nose*, *black blizzard*, *meringue storm*, *cat's paw*).

The names of Canadian winds are not all well known and may not be exclusive to Canada. While some wind names have endured and are used in daily conversation, others have been dropped, forgotten or changed. The following list, by no means complete, is a sampling:

- *barber*: a strong wind carrying precipitation that freezes upon contact, especially on the face and hair
- *black blizzard*: a dust storm of black prairie soil
- *break-up wind*: a spring wind that hastens the break-up of ice in northern rivers and lakes
- *cold maker*: a cold north wind
- *cow storm*: a gale on Ellesmere Island so strong that "it blows the horns off the [muskoxen] cows"
- *dally*: a sudden slackening, shifting of the wind
- *dwigh* (*dwey*, *dwoy*): a sudden shower or snowstorm in Newfoundland, accompanied by strong winds
- *fairy*: a strong, sudden gust of wind on an otherwise calm day
- *flaw*: a sudden gust or squall
- *ground-drifter*: a cold north wind that creates ground snowdrifts
- *haboob* (*Arabic origin*): a prairie duststorm characterized by rounded projections along the front edge of the advancing wall of dust

- *lambkiller*: a severe sudden storm in March just after lambs are born
- *liner*: a strong wind or gale at the time of the fall equinox
- *out-wind*: a wind blowing seaward off the land
- *plow wind*: strong downdraft associated with squall lines and thunderstorms and with the force of a tornado
- *scud*: a sudden gust of wind
- *Sheila's blush, or brush*: a fierce wind and heavy snowstorm around St. Patrick's Day
- *snow devil*: a whirling column of snow sucked up in a vortex by the wind
- *Squamish*: a violent outflow from Squamish, British Columbia, along Howe Sound and through the channels around Bowen Island
- *wreckhouse*: an extremely fierce wind in western Newfoundland noted for blowing trains off tracks and trucks off roads
- *Yoho blow*: a strong, cold wind in the Yoho Valley in the Rocky Mountains

> ❄ Alberta clippers were named after the clipper sailing ships, which at one time were the fastest vessels on the seas. The storms zip along at 64 kilometres per hour, preceded by about five centimetres of light, powdery snow and followed by violent winds capable of reaching 100 kilometres per hour. This combination of conditions often results in severe blowing and drifting with blizzard conditions that can leave many roads impassable.

LEGEND OF A FURRY WEATHER PROPHET

EVERY YEAR ON FEBRUARY 2, WINTER-WEARY NORTH Americans pin their hopes for fair weather on a furry, burrow-dwelling rodent.

❄ According to their keepers, Wiarton Willie from the Bruce Peninsula area of Ontario is credited with 90 percent accuracy in making weather prognostications. Gary the ground-hog from Kleinburg, north of Toronto, boasts a forecast success rate of 70 percent.

Groundhogs command national attention on network news and in front-page headlines when they make their annual midwinter weather prediction. So revered are these pug-nosed creatures that in 1987, the foremost forecaster of them all, Punxsutawney Phil from Penn-sylvania, was invited by then President Reagan to the Oval Office to mark the centennial of Phil's and his forebears' weather forecasting.

According to legend, the groundhog emerges from its burrow precisely at noon on February 2 to look for its shadow. If it is a sunny day and the groundhog sees its shadow, it returns to its hole to sleep, and winter continues for six more weeks. (Not bad news by most Canadian standards!) If it does not see its shadow, it remains outside because the worst of winter is over and warmer weather is on the way.

In fact, there is a grain of truth to the shadow aspect of the legend. Sunny days in winter are generally associated with colder, drier arctic air, and cloudy days with milder, moist maritime air. Given the tendency for weather con-ditions to persist for several days, the weather on any Feb-ruary 2 may continue the same for a few days, but not necessarily longer than that.

Can a groundhog actually predict the length of winter? Groundhog Day organizers boast that the rodents' fore-casts are accurate 75 to 90 percent of the time. However, meteorological records prove that the groundhogs' success rate is quite low. A study of weather data over the past 30 to 40 years for 13 cities across Canada reveals there was an equal number of cloudy and sunny days on February 2. During that period, the groundhogs' predictions were right only 37 percent of the time. Indeed, for nearly two-thirds of the years the groundhogs' forecasts turned out to be wrong. Given that a 33-percent accuracy can occur by chance, a score of 37 percent is nothing to boast about! The truth is that proverbs, sayings or superstitions that tie weather events on one date to the weather on particular days or months ahead are generally useless.

Falling halfway between the winter solstice and the spring equinox, February 2 has been celebrated in folklore for centuries as the day to turn our backs on winter and begin looking forward to spring. In medieval Europe, Groundhog Day was known as Candlemas Day, a Christian festival named for the custom of lighting candles on that day. Several rhymes describe how the weather on Candlemas foretells the weather for the following weeks. One rhyme goes like this:

> If Candlemas Day be fair and bright;
> Winter will have another flight,
> But if Candlemas Day brings cloud and rain,
> Winter is gone and won't come again.

In Germany, there is a saying that a shepherd would rather see a wolf enter his stable on Candlemas Day than the sun. In France, country folk warn that a sunny Candlemas means another winter is on the way, while in Spain, a wet February 2 means the cold is over for the season. Europeans observed that such hibernating animals as the hedgehog and badger began to stir on warm winter days around early February, so they assigned the job of weather prophet to them.

When settlers came to North America, they brought the February 2 legend with them. The fact that there were no hedgehogs was not a problem. The behaviour of groundhogs, marmots and other rodents was so similar that they were conscripted to provide the forecast. Groundhogs are frequently seen in the woodlands of southern Canada from the Maritimes to the Peace River region, and across the northern United States and in Alaska; thus, the role of spring harbinger fell to them and the day was renamed in their honour. Groundhogs are not native to British Columbia, but the hoary marmot and the yellow-bellied marmot are close cousins which have been assigned weather-forecasting duties there.

❄ Punxsutawney Phil began his forecasting in 1896 at Punxsutawney, Pennsylvania, a town 150 kilometres northeast of Pittsburg. According to the Smithsonian Institute, seven men from Punxsutawney decided to climb a local hill called Gobbler's Nob to drink liquor and eat groundhogs cooked over a campfire. They had such a good time that they decided to do it every year. The local newspaper editor called the group the Punxsutawney Groundhog Club and declared the community to be the weather capital of the world.

Early settlers hoped for signs of an early spring so they could begin planting and shorten the time to harvest, especially with winter provisions dwindling. They wanted the groundhog to emerge and stay outside as a prediction of coming warmth. For them, the weather on February 2 was a reverse indicator: sunshine (good weather), with shadows to frighten the animal, meant bad weather to come; a cloudy day (bad weather) prevented shadows so the furry creature could leave its den without fear, foretelling early warmth.

What these settlers did not realize was that the groundhog sleeps later than the European hedgehog and is less likely to stir even on warm winter days. When February 2 rolls around, the worst of winter's weather is usually over in western Europe, but not in Canada. In early February, the openings to groundhog burrows are usually buried under deep layers of snow and ice.

Wiarton Willie of Wiarton, Ontario, near Georgian Bay, is unlikely to appear above ground until roughly mid-March, six to eight weeks after his special day. Brandon Bob of Manitoba sleeps till late March or early April. According to groundhog expert and zoology professor Dr. Edward Bailey of the University of Guelph, when the mature male groundhog finally arouses from hibernation and surfaces, he does not look for his shadow, nor even for food, but rather travels from burrow to burrow searching for a mate. Since the female emerges from her cosy den several weeks later, males bide their time fighting territorial battles with other males.

Needless to say, the Groundhog Day legend is pure

GROUNDHOG FORECASTS		
	Chance of Groundhog seeing its Shadow (percent)	Correct Groundhog Forecasts* (percent)
St. John's	53	41
Charlottetown	50	41
Halifax	50	42
Fredericton	48	34
Montreal	52	36
Toronto	54	29
Ottawa	48	42
Winnipeg	78	30
Regina	63	38
Edmonton	60	26
Vancouver	23	35
Whitehorse	43	42
Yellowknife	50	50

* Correct just by accident or chance — 33 percent of the time.

superstition. Indeed, the sight of people in tuxedos and top hats trying to coax a groundhog out of a hole on February 2 for any sign that will provide a precise weather forecast for the next six weeks is about as silly as anything can get — pure "ground hogwash!"

Probably few people really believe the groundhog myth. Still it lives on and provides us with an opportunity to celebrate the fact that winter is at least half over. For some communities, Groundhog Day is an important tourist attraction, and a good reason for a midwinter party. For the lowly groundhog — more often seen as a bane to farmers, gardeners and highway crews — it represents his "15 minutes" of fame.

Handler John Makela holds Wiarton Willie after the albino groundhog failed to see its shadow in 1989. CANAPRESS

SUMMER'S LAST STAND

SOMETIME BETWEEN LABOUR DAY AND REMEMBRANCE Day — after the first killing frost and before the first lasting snow cover — most regions of southern Canada experience an interlude of delightfully warm, sunny, dry weather called Indian summer. It is a time when balmy temperatures and hard frosts are apt to occur on the same day. Some years it passes us by, but usually it occurs in two or three episodes, tantalizing us with one last taste of summer before winter sets in.

True Indian summer must meet certain criteria. It must be sunny and dry, and unseasonably warm but not really hot. Early morning mist or fog is sometimes prevalent, and the atmosphere is often hazy blue or smoky. Air pressure is usually high and steady, and the wind is either calm or light.

The expression *Indian summer* is peculiar to North America, even though weatherlore suggests this warm fall weather also occurs in Europe. Europeans took to naming this period after whichever saint's day it coincided with. For the French, St. Martin's summer begins on November 11. Swedish legend refers to All Saints Rest, a stretch of warm, clear weather commencing on November 1. The British sometimes called it Old Wives' summer, while the Germans talked about Old Woman's summer, and the Russians Peasant Woman's summer. The English also refer to St. Luke's little summer about October 18.

> ❄ The Toronto Meteorological Observatory recorded the date of certain periodic events, such as Indian summer, until 1871. Almost invariably, its records show that Indian summer occurred in late October or the first half of November and lasted from a few days to about a week.

❄ Indian summer weatherlore: "If we do not get our Indian summer in October or November, we shall get it in the winter."

Some early writers gave this interlude a definite beginning and ending. American writer Henry David Thoreau wrote in his diaries that Indian summer weather occurred anytime between September 27 and December 13. An old adage states that if All Saints' (November 1) brings out winter, St. Martin's (November 11) brings out Indian summer. If that weatherlore is true, Indian summer would be unlikely in Canada in any year.

In North America, the term *Indian summer* has been used for more than two centuries, although its origins are uncertain. One of the earliest Canadian references seems to have been made in 1796 by Elizabeth Simcoe, wife of the first lieutenant-governor of Upper Canada. In her diary she wrote: "There is a fog like our Indian summer, with insufferable heat" . . .

An even earlier reference was made in 1778 by Joseph Doddridge, a backwoods preacher who travelled in the hills of Virginia and Pennsylvania during the time of the American Revolution. In his book *Settlements and Indian Wars*, he wrote that throughout the summer, a band of native Americans would harass the settlers, probably in the hope that the settlers would leave the area. When cold weather arrived in the fall, they would usually return to their villages and the skirmishes would end. However, when a spell of unseasonable warmth returned in the late fall, the fighting would resume. The settlers called this time Indian summer.

Over the years, many writers have proposed other explanations for the origin of the expression, some more plausible than others. The most probable explanation is that some North American native people relied on this benign fall weather to harvest their late crops of corn and pumpkins, and to prepare for winter. Another theory attributes the blue haze of the fall season to the smoke from grass and brush fires set by native groups on the Prairies. The smoke provided cover for hunters and was used to direct game to a prescribed area. Some people claim the term applies to the season when deciduous trees were dressed as colourfully as native people.

An entirely different interpretation suggests British mariners used the expression to describe the dry, hazy weather prevalent in India during the retreating southwest monsoons in October and November. Early European travellers may have recognized a similar spell of weather in North America and called it Indian summer.

Although there is no universally accepted definition of Indian summer, it is characterized by more than simply warm fall days. Stormy weather, a frost or, in some extreme cases, a dusting of snow (Inuit summer) precede true Indian summer. Pioneers discovered that freezing temperatures or storms arrived around the fall equinox (on or about September 23). These periods of nasty weather were referred to as "half winter." Only after they had passed could Indian summer begin. Indian summer weather can therefore be defined as three or more consecutive days with at least five hours of bright sunshine, afternoon temperature of 15°C or higher, and no precipitation.

The meteorological conditions responsible for this weather arise when a large high-pressure system stagnates over eastern North America, and a clockwise circulation of air around the high moves warm air from the Gulf of Mexico into the central or eastern portion of the continent. Calm conditions or light winds prevail, causing an atmospheric buildup of pollutants and dust responsible for the bluish haze prevalent at this time of year. The warm, sunny weather may linger for a week or more as storms skirt the high-pressure system, but Indian summer usually ends abruptly when an invasion of cold northern air reminds us winter is on its way.

In some years Indian summer passes us by, but most regions of southern Canada enjoy at least one spell of it each fall. Other years may have two or more distinct episodes, separated by dull, cold, wet weather.

Based on 40 years of meteorological data, the first Indian summer weather usually begins during the last week of September or in the first few days of October in central Canada, ten days earlier in the West, and two weeks earlier in the Maritimes. Although this "fifth season" rarely recurs at the same time every year, its most likely dates, average duration and probability of occurrence in Edmonton, Winnipeg, Toronto, Montreal and Fredericton have been determined.

The most probable dates in Fredericton fall between September 12 and 24. And although New Brunswick's capital tends to have more warm spells than the other cities, they are generally short-lived. With weather systems bombarding the Maritimes from virtually every direction, there is only a 25-percent chance Indian summer will last five days or more.

The warm weather generally arrives later in Montreal — October 1 to 18 on average. In fact, both Montreal and Fredericton experienced one of the latest warm spells in the last 40 years, from November 18 to 20, 1953. Daytime highs of 17°C in Montreal and 19°C in Fredericton set records for those dates.

The most probable time in Winnipeg is September 13 to 20, with a 45 percent chance of the fine weather lasting at least five days. The longest Indian summers in the city stretched over 22 days in 1963 and 20 days in 1962. Winnipeg also has the most consistent record — only twice in 38 years did Indian summer fail to materialize.

Edmontonians can expect a warm spell about three

years in four, with September 19 to 26 the most likely dates. The good weather usually persists for more than six days, the longest average duration for the cities sampled. But few Indian summers can match the one Torontonians experienced in October 1963: 23 consecutive days, with daytime highs above 23°C for 17 of those days, and a record high of 29.4°C on October 6. On average, however, Indian summer in Toronto has a 50-percent chance of lasting more than five days, with September 23 to 29 and October 13 to 22 the most likely times.

❋ It is not the first frost that causes leaves of deciduous trees to change colour. As the days become shorter, the growth process in the leaves slows to a stop. As the chlorophyll content decreases, the green pigment in the foliage slowly disappears, allowing the yellow, brown, orange and other pigments in the leaves to show through.

Because frosts occur much later, and in some years not at all, in Victoria and Vancouver, Indian summer is not generally mentioned along the Pacific Coast. However, any spell of pleasant, dry sunny weather that interrupts the wet season for a few days is sometimes referred to as Indian summer.

Although Indian summer offers some of the finest weather of the year, the lack of precipitation may cause a resumption of forest fires. The unseasonable warmth also sends false messages to migrating birds, hibernating animals and spring plants.

Some of the worst episodes of smog coincide with this time, because the stable atmospheric conditions and sinking air associated with high-pressure systems prevent pollutants from dispersing. Hospital admission records indicate this contributes to a dramatic rise in serious eye infections, while the numbers of people suffering from asthma, bronchitis, and other respiratory disorders rises as well. In one such episode in late October 1989, the air pollution index rose to 73 in Toronto and 50 in Montreal for four consecutive days. An index of 35 is considered serious, and industries are encouraged to reduce emissions voluntarily.

For the most part, though, Indian summer is a welcome time of year, a short but sweet season that is ideal for one last canoe trip or hike before the snow flies.

HOW COLD CAN IT GET?

AT 7:20 A.M., FEBRUARY 3, 1947, GORDON TOOLE left the warm interior of the weather station at Snag Airport, 30 kilometres east of the Alaska–Yukon boundary, to take the morning temperature reading. He noticed that the alcohol in the thermometer had fallen below the last gradation on the scale. (Because mercury freezes at –39°C, alcohol thermometers must be used in the winter.) Toole scratched the side of the thermometer sheath to mark the low point: –64.4°C. When the thermometer was recalibrated three months later in Toronto, it was found to be reading in error by almost 1.5°C. The weather service accepted the figure of –63°C as the lowest official temperature ever recorded in Canada. It is also a record for North America.

❄ Fifteen-year-old Chester Greenwood invented ear muffs in 1873. He asked his grandmother to sew chunks of beaver fur onto the ends of a wire because he was tired of freezing his ears while skating.

For more than a week before that February day, cold air from northeastern Siberia had been stalled over the Yukon. Skies were clear, winds calm, visibility unlimited and 38 centimetres of snow lay on the ground.

Staff at the combined Royal Canadian Mounted Police and weather station recalled that, during the cold spell, audibility increased so much that one could literally eavesdrop on distant conversations and hear dogs barking in the village five kilometres northeast of the airport. During very cold weather, both the intensity and audibility of sound increases because most of the sound waves are confined near the earth's surface. Thus, sounds usually heard 30 metres away can be heard more than a kilometre away.

Throughout the cold snap, there was intense radio static, much like the crackling during a thunderstorm, and the moist breath from husky dogs condensed instantly in the cold, dry air and hovered in fog patches for several days above the teams. An exhaled breath of air made a hissing sound as it froze and created vapor trails that extended 100 to 500 metres above the ground for three or four minutes before disappearing. All water lines in the log barracks froze. Washing was limited to once a day, with a total ban on showers and baths. Exposed skin froze in less than three minutes.

How cold can it get and why? The lowest natural temperature ever recorded at the earth's surface was –89.6°C at the (then) Soviet scientific station Vostok in Antarctica on July 21, 1983. (At such low temperatures, electrical-resistance thermometers calibrated down to –90°C are used; resistance to the passage of electrical current through a wire is affected by the temperature of the wire.) The coldest place inhabited year-round is Oymyakon, a village of 600 in northeastern Siberia. In February 1964, the weather station recorded a low of –71°C.

During the prolonged darkness of winter, the air over the huge snow and ice-covered surfaces of Canada, Siberia and Alaska may stagnate for weeks, radiating heat to outer space. Air over the northern lands becomes colder than that over the Arctic Ocean because some heat is conducted upward through the ice cover. The earth's surface loses more heat to the sky than it receives from the sun, and as a result, the ground surface grows colder, cooling the air immediately above it. This cooling continues upward, with the air layers closest to the ground remaining the coldest. The rate of cooling is greatest in dry air conditions under clear skies with calm or light winds. The outcome is a condition known as an atmospheric inversion — where temperatures increase rather than decrease with height — that covers the entire arctic region for much of the winter.

As the arctic high-pressure system intensifies, the cold air naturally moves to areas of lower pressure and pushes southward across the middle of the continent. Often a low-pressure system moving from the West will draw the cold arctic air into the rear of a developing storm, causing strong winds, blowing snow and rapidly falling temperatures. These cold fronts curve across the Prairies and cause most of the winter weather in central and Eastern Canada.

❄ Until 1947, the lowest temperature in Canada was –61.7°C at Fort Good Hope on the Mackenzie River.

No part of Canada is immune to winter's deep-freeze. Only Vancouver Island and the southwest coast of British Columbia have average winter temperatures above the freezing mark. However, even Vancouver and Victoria are not without their cold weather legends. At the end of December 1968, and again during the last two weeks of January 1969, cold arctic air penetrated British Columbia's mountain passes and reached the west coast. Beginning on Boxing Day and persisting for 11 days, Vancouver's temperature remained below freezing. On Sunday morning, December 29, the thermometer's mercury hit bottom at –17.8°C, the lowest ever recorded at Vancouver.

Eureka, on Ellesmere Island, Northwest Territories, is Canada's coldest weather station. The average annual temperature is –19.7°C, but in February, usually the coldest month, Eureka's average temperature is –38°C. In February 1979, it recorded the lowest average monthly temperature ever in Canada or North America, a numbing –47°C. For 17 days, the thermometer stayed below –45°C. On the 15th, the station also eclipsed its previous all-time low with a reading of –55.3°C. The seasoned staff at Eureka took the cold spell in stride. Stress, which might have been aggravated by the monotonous cold, was mitigated by two saving events: on the 21st, the sun made its first appearance on the southern horizon, without question the most heralded event of an arctic winter; and on the 28th, the solar eclipse was visible to the south of Eureka through a heavy bank of ice fog.

A long-standing cold weather legend is that the

Legend has it that the coldest corner in Canada is at Portage Avenue and Main Street in Winnipeg.

WESTERN CANADA PICTORIAL INDEX

coldest corner in Canada is at Portage Avenue and Main Street in downtown Winnipeg. Not so! Some Winnipeggers will tell you that it is not even the coldest in Winnipeg. The truth is that there are no official temperature measurements at any street corner in Canada to confirm the coldest intersection. Winnipeg's city centre is usually three or four degrees warmer than the airport, owing to the urban heat-island effect. The lowest reading at the airport was –45°C on February 18, 1966, but airports in Edmonton, Regina and Saskatoon have all recorded lower temperatures.

❄ If skin becomes cold enough, ice crystals form and damage tissue. Ears, nose, hands and feet are the most vulnerable parts of the body. Serious cases of frostbite can lead to extreme sensitivity to cold that can last for years. In the most serious cases, amputation may be necessary.

Another Canadian cold-weather myth purports that White River, Ontario, a small town on the Canadian Pacific Railway north of Lake Superior between Marathon and Chapleau, is the coldest place in Canada. White River does have a legitimate claim to fame as the birthplace of Winnie the Pooh (Winnie was a bear cub from White River named for Winnipeg and taken to a London zoo where it impressed Christopher Robin and inspired his father, A.A. Milne). But White River is not even the coldest place in Ontario, let alone Canada. That notoriety belongs to Iroquois Falls which, at –58.3°C, has the lowest temperature ever officially reported by any station in Eastern Canada. That record also makes White River look almost mild by comparison. Its coldest temperature is –51.7°C, recorded on January 23, 1935 — the eighth coldest reading in Ontario.

One of Alberta's most infamous cold weather events occurred in the winter of 1968–69 when Edmontonians shivered through the city's longest cold spell on record. On January 7, the temperature plunged below –18°C and

A fall scene along the Rivière Noire in Quebec.
VICTORIA HURST/FIRST LIGHT

Lightning illuminates a grain elevator.
DAVE REEDE/FIRST LIGHT

Fog blankets the valleys near St. John's, Newfoundland.
DALE WILSON/FIRST LIGHT

A hailstorm near Erickson, Manitoba.

Towering cumulus clouds with streaks of rain below.
DAVE REEDE/FIRST LIGHT

Above: Altocumulus
clouds in tufts.
MIKE GRANDMAISON/
FIRST LIGHT

Left: Cirrocumulus
clouds.
DALE WILSON/FIRST LIGHT

Noon in late January at the Upper Air Observing Station
at Mould Bay, N.W.T.
D.G. Tesch

Ice-covered wild rose hips on Prince Edward Island.
John Sylvester/First Light

A young visitor tastes the sap at a sugar bush in Ontario.
BRIAN MILNE/FIRST LIGHT

The northern lights.
LEE SNYDER, GEOPHYSICAL INSTITUTE, UNIVERSITY OF ALASKA FAIRBANKS

A rainbow arches across a spring sky
north of Tara, Ontario.
G. ROCK

stayed cold for 26 consecutive days until the afternoon of February 2. Planeloads of sunseekers escaped to warmer climes in Cuba, Mexico and the Canary Islands. Apart from down-filled jackets, retail sales in Edmonton were way down, but taxis and tow trucks were in great demand. For the thousands of residents who stayed home and endured the cold, the *Edmonton Journal* issued survival certificates claiming "I lived through Edmonton's record cold spell."

❄ The average temperature year-round in Canada is –5.6°C, making it the coldest country in the world.

January 1982 was one of the coldest months in recent memory. Almost the entire country was in the grip of a month-long record cold spell with temperatures below –40°C in most provinces. The prolonged cold resulted in the breakdown of numerous diesel trucks and trains, and innumerable school closings for two or three days at a time. Despite some of the best snow conditions in years, outdoor recreation was discouraged due to the dangerous wind chill.

Even more brutal were the winter months of January 1950 across the West and February 1934 in the East. In January 1950, one of the coldest air masses ever to descend on this country persisted for most of the month across much of western Canada. Temperatures from Vancouver to Winnipeg tumbled to a 20th-century low, some 18 degrees below normal. Readings approaching –50°C or lower were recorded on the Prairies and in the North, records that are unequalled today.

❄ On average, the lowest temperatures of the year occur from January 8 to 15 in western Canada and from February 3 to 7 in eastern Canada.

The cold onslaught of February 1934, with –30°C readings or less, engulfed the continent from Manitoba to the Atlantic seaboard and down the east coast to Palm

Beach, Florida. Most residents of the East talked of little else but the weather and did their best to keep indoors. Ice trapped fishing vessels off Nova Scotia, overheated stoves ignited fires in Quebec, and officials cancelled amateur hockey games in Ontario. Plumbers, mechanics and coal dealers were kept busy everywhere. It was so cold that the wheels on some cars being towed would not turn. Hospitals cared for countless victims suffering from frostbite or cold-burned lungs. To avoid freezing, milk bottles were delivered personally rather than placed in milk boxes or left outside doors. Near Ingersoll, Ontario, workers stopped taking ice from the Thames River for home delivery because the channel through which the cakes of ice were floated kept freezing over.

The cold over the relatively warm waters of the Niagara River produced a dense cloud that concealed the falls from viewing. An ice bridge formed in the lower Niagara River, and for only the second time in 100 years, Lake Ontario froze over. While some tried skating from Hamilton to Toronto and back, as far as is known, no one tried skating, skiing or walking across the lake. The only other occasion that Lake Ontario completely froze over was during the winter of 1874–75. Extreme cold and heavy snow were tolerated then, because sleighing was the sole method of winter travel, other than railways.

The year 1972 was unusual in that the entire country reported colder than normal temperatures. Usually in a vast country such as Canada, weather is so varied that a cold East is balanced by a warm West, a cold North by a warm South or vice versa. But in 1972, for the only year in 50 years sampled, temperatures were below normal throughout Canada. The winter from December 1971 to March 1972 rated near the top among severe winters in the 20th century. It was especially cold in the eastern

Arctic, subarctic and the Yukon. Monthly temperatures were more than 10°C below normal. The abnormal cold contributed to about 10 times the normal number of icebergs reported by early July off the eastern shore of Canada.

Cold-weather superlatives abound in Canada. For example, of cities in the world over 500,000, Winnipeg has the coldest midwinter temperature. Ottawa is the second coldest national capital, next to Ulaanbaatar, Mongolia. Overall, Canada is the coldest country in the world: an average of all the daily temperature observations year-round works out to a chilling −5.6°C. But take comfort, Canada; it is colder in Greenland, Siberia and Antarctica.

TOP COLD SPOTS			
Province/ Territory	°C	Date	Location
Yukon Territory	−63.0	Feb. 3, 1947	Snag
Northwest Territories	−61.7	Dec. 31, 1910	Fort Good Hope
Alberta	−61.1	Jan. 11, 1911	Fort Vermilion
British Columbia	−58.9	Jan. 31, 1947	Smith River
Ontario	−58.3	Jan. 23, 1935	Iroquois Falls
Saskatchewan	−56.7	Feb. 1., 1893	Prince Albert
Quebec	−54.4	Feb. 5, 1923	Doucet
Manitoba	−52.8	Jan. 9, 1899	Norway House
Newfoundland and Labrador	−51.1	Feb. 17, 1973	Esker 2
New Brunswick	−47.2	Feb. 1, 1955	Sisson Dam
Nova Scotia	−41.1	Jan. 31, 1920	Upper Stewiacke
Prince Edward Island	−37.2	Jan. 26, 1884	Kilmahumaig

AW, C'MON, CANADIAN WINTERS AREN'T SO BAD

F EW COUNTRIES' CLIMATES HAVE BEEN SO MALIGNED AS Canada's. American weather reporters consistently heap scorn on us as they glibly go on about "Alberta clippers, Saskatchewan slashers and Manitoba mashers" moving down from Canada. The truth is that most of Canada's nastiest weather (if not its coldest) comes from the United States — monster snows, freezing rains, hurricanes and steam-bath humidity are all American imports.

❄ The rotary snow shovel (forerunner of the modern snowblower) was invented in 1869 by Dr. J.W. Elliot, a Toronto dentist.

❄ The weight of one cubic metre of old, accumulated snow in Winnipeg is 190 kilograms; in Quebec City 220 kilograms; and in Whistler, British Columbia, 430 kilograms. The weights vary because of the difference in moisture content of the snow.

To add insult to injury, most Canadians believe this hyperbole. Artist Harold Town once said, "We are a nation of thermometers monitoring cold fronts . . . We jig to the crunch of snow." Political columnist Don Braid called Canada "a confederation of crummy climates." And humorist Gary Lautens said you can always pick a Canadian man out of a crowd, "He's the one with salt stains halfway up his trousers."

Much of our climatological infamy results from our long and severe winters. Any time between November and March, news film and front-page stories feature city residents struggling against winter's latest paralysing storm, blasting winds and numbing cold.

There is no denying that in most parts of Canada winter comes early, is harsh and stays late. It is the dominant season, lasting one or two months longer than its astronomical allotment. Freezing days outnumber frost-free ones and more than a third of the year's precipitation falls as snow (the world average is five percent). The only national capital colder than Ottawa is Ulaanbaatar, Mongolia; Winnipeg is the coldest of all cities with a population over a half-million; and Montrealers shovel more snow than any other city in the world.

Despite these frigid facts, the myth that winter is nothing but a pain, a curse and a catastrophe has persisted for too long. People's minds are so fixed on this image that we think of winter in terms of extremes, and synthesize the whole season from the worst days of winter: four to six months of fierce blizzards, dirty slush piles, shin-high soakers, flesh-freezing wind chill, drifting and blowing snow, ice, fog, and icy roads and sidewalks. But in reality, more often than not, a typical Canadian winter day is invigorating, likeable and livable.

Moreover, Canadian winters vary greatly from place to place and from year to year. In the settled south, some places never experience cold winds, slush and blowing snow during the year, whereas others endure winter as the longest season, even in the mildest year. Along the Pacific coast, winter arrives with persistently cool, wet and foggy weather. In the Arctic, winter is cold and dark, with little precipitation. Mid-latitude continental areas are subject to more frequent and intense storms, as well as fluctuating spells of long-lasting cold and abbreviated mildness. In 1969, Edmontonians survived a record cold winter — 26 consecutive days below –18°C. Yet in 1984, Edmonton had

> ❄ The price of a suit of long underwear in 1910 was 96 cents. In 1993, it was $24.99.
>
> ❄ The number of Canadian households in 1988 with snowblowers was 1,089,000 and air conditioners 1,689,000.

> ❄ Ten percent of all salt produced in the world is used to clear highways in North America.

the mildest January-to-March period on record, more than 7°C above normal, and milder than Toronto that year.

Even a city with a reputation as chilling as Winnipeg does not have more than 40 "misery days" during an average winter. By comparison, winter weather woes should not be a preoccupation more than once a week on average in Ottawa, Edmonton or Vancouver. A winter misery day may have more than 10 centimetres of snow on the same day; several hours of blowing snow, cold rain or freezing rain; a wind chill that freezes skin in two minutes; deep slush (more than five centimetres of snow and five millimetres of rain on the same day); or be the fourth day in a row with overcast skies (each subsequent day also counts as one). These criteria were selected following discussions with meteorologists living in different parts of southern Canada.

❋ Canadians spend more money on skiing than on snow removal. On the other hand, the snow removal budget for Montreal is $50 million. The city removes more snow from its streets than any other city in the world — more than 42 million tonnes on average each year.

Canadians have considerably different opinions about what weather misery means. A day with light snow, moderate wind and a −10°C temperature in Vancouver would result in discomfort for Vancouverites. However, such weather in Saskatoon or Thunder Bay would hardly be noticed.

Opinion as to what is miserable would also vary widely depending on age, health, outlook and degree or acclimatization; the timing of an event (weekend, rush hour, end of winter); the cumulative effect (successive storms); and local services and structures (effectiveness of snow removal, number of bus shelters, sky walks and underground tunnels).

An analysis of winters from 1953 to 1990 showed that Ottawa recorded on average only 19 misery days a year, and a range from seven to 36 days over the 38 winters. Winnipeg nearly doubled that average, enduring 37 misery days, or a quarter of the winter. The hardest winter for Winnipeggers must have been in 1965 when 68 days had "stay-at-home" weather.

❋ Quebec City and Calgary are our ski capitals with more skiers per household than any other cities in Canada.

The wind chill factor accounts for more than 60 percent of tough winter days in Edmonton and Winnipeg. At the same time, less than five percent of Winnipeg's winter misery comes from consecutive sunless days. Most Canadian cities, in fact, are positioned considerably farther south than their Eurasian twins and enjoy considerably more daylight and sunshine during the winter. Indeed, a sunny day can make all the difference between soaring spirits or the urge to fly south in search of summer.

Vancouver's winter misery comes principally from extended cloudy periods and cold, rainy days, conditions most red-nosed easterners are quick to point out are not to their liking. Ottawa's winter misery comes equally from heavy snowfall, blowing snow, freezing rain and severe wind chill. Quebec City lives up to its reputation as one of the snowiest metropolises in the world. There, most winter misery days result from heavy snow and blowing snow, but also from wind chill, which accounts for about a quarter of them. Halifax experiences more continental than marine weather with most of its misery coming from heavy snow, wind chill and blowing snow, and relatively little from slush and sunless days.

❋ Montreal's average daily temperature in January is similar to Moscow's; the city has the same average annual temperature as Stockholm.

Differences in the number of weather misery days between successive winters can be dramatic. And for all six cities

WINTER MISERY WEATHER, 1953–90

City	Average Number of Winter Misery Days (November–March)	Worst Month(s)
Halifax	25	January/February
Quebec City	33	January
Ottawa	19	December
Winnipeg	37	January
Edmonton	15	January
Vancouver	12	January

City	Major Cause(s) of Weather Misery	Range of Misery Days Low (Yr) to High (Yr)
Halifax	wind chill	7 (1983) to 66 (1956)
Quebec City	heavy, blowing snow	14(1980) to 59 (1963)
Ottawa	heavy snow, wind chill, freezing rain, blowing snow	7 (1990) to 36 (1971)
Winnipeg	wind chill	16 (1975) to 68 (1965)
Edmonton	wind chill	3 (1987) to 55 (1972)
Vancouver	lack of sunshine, cold rain	3 (1988) to 37 (1969)

examined, the 1980s had the fewest average number of winter misery days. Days when three or more of the misery conditions occurred together are rare.

Overall, we tend to greatly exaggerate the unpleasant

Cutting wood in the winter of 1869 on Craig Street in Montreal. ONTARIO ARCHIVES

aspects of winter. Harsh days are surprisingly few, no more than four to seven per month on average, and certainly not the season-long ice age that one would expect in the Great White North, eh!

WEATHER
ACROSS CANADA

CANADIAN WEATHER HONOURS

WEATHER SUPERLATIVES, SUCH AS THE COLDEST, THE wettest, and the windiest, applied to places in Canada have always been of interest to Canadians. Unlike lists of the world's best- and worst-dressed people and other end-of-the-year recitals of people, places and events, weather honours serve a useful purpose beyond satisfying curiosity or settling disputes. Knowing which place has the coldest temperature, the heaviest snowfall or the brightest skies is important to Chambers of Commerce, tourism and convention bureaus and advertising agencies; to those seeking havens from weather for retirement or health problems; or to weather buffs simply seeking more climate trivia.

Determining which place has the best, worst, most or least of anything depends largely on the criteria selected. No simple statistic can identify, for instance, the coldest town in Canada. Various criteria may be chosen, so that any selected or devised definition becomes arbitrary. And enough categories could be found to keep the assorted communities happy that want to proclaim themselves the frigid capital of Canada.

Let's consider the coldest place. Should it have the coldest day, month, winter or year on average, or on record? Should the coldest place in the nation

❄ Welcoming signs at city limits as seen through the eyes of a climatologist: Welcome to London, Ontario, "The Sound and Light Capital of Canada"; Winnipeg, "The City with the Sunniest Winters in Canada"; Prince Rupert, "The Cloudiest and Wettest City in Canada"; Penticton, "A Fog-free City"; and Ottawa, "The Snowiest and Coldest Major Capital in the World."

have the longest spell of low temperatures or of severe wind chills? Would a better criterion for defining coldness be the greatest number of days per year with below-zero temperatures? Certainly, one or two cold winters do not permanently define the country's coldest spot. Unfortunately, long-term records exist for fewer than 30 sites.

An analysis was done to identify Canadian communities that rate a weather superlative. Weather categories were chosen using long-term average conditions represented by the climatological normal. A normal, as defined by the United Nation's World Meteorological Organization, is simply an average of weather components: for example, temperature, precipitation or pressure over a period of 30 consecutive years. In early 1993, Environment Canada completed a new set of climatological normals for 1,600 weather stations across the country covering the period from 1961 to 1990.

For a place to boast weather supremacy, it must have a properly sited weather station close by where official Environment Canada instruments are used and standard observing procedures are followed. In the accompanying analysis, 75 Canadian cities with a population of at least 10,000 people and a nearby weather station, preferably an airport location, were chosen.

Higher amounts of snowfall, colder temperatures and stronger winds have occurred in many smaller communities not included in the list. Small, out-of-the-way hamlets, such as Stewart, British Columbia, with some 670 centimetres of snow annually, or Argentia, Newfoundland, with 206 foggy days a year, are the weather champions in Canada for their respective elements. But in terms of the greatest number of people affected by weather, only the 75 largest cities in Canada were considered. By limiting it to these centres, almost 70 percent of the population of Canada is included.

135

Snow in midsummer at Arcola, Saskatchewan, in 1903.
SASKATCHEWAN ARCHIVES BOARD

CANADIAN WEATHER HONOURS

Warmest Summers		Kelowna	26.4
(average daytime temperature		Medicine Hat	26.0
(°C) during June, July and		St. Catharines	25.7
August)		Estevan	25.7
Kamloops	27.2	Moose Jaw	25.6
Penticton	26.9	Chateauguay	25.5
Windsor	26.5	Sorel	25.3

Coldest Winters
(average nighttime temperature, °C, during December,
January and February)

Yellowknife	−29.9
Thompson	−28.6
Prince Albert	−23.8
Fort McMurray	−22.9
Brandon	−21.8
Timmins	−21.7
Yorkton	−21.6
Val-d'Or	−21.3
Winnipeg	−21.2
Saskatoon	−20.7

Coldest Places
(lowest annual average
temperature °C)

Yellowknife	−5.2
Thompson	−3.4
Whitehorse	−1.0
Fort McMurray	0.2
Prince Albert	0.5
Sept-Iles	0.9
Timmins	1.2
Val-d'Or	1.2
Yorkton	1.4
Baie-Comeau	1.5

Warmest Places
(highest annual average
temperature, °C)

Vancouver	9.9
Victoria	9.5
Windsor	9.1
Penticton	9.0
St. Catharines	8.9
Kamloops	8.6
Sarnia	8.0
Hamilton	7.6
Belleville	7.5
Toronto	7.2

Snowiest Cities
(annual average snowfall
in centimetres)

Sept-Iles	415
Corner Brook	414
Moncton	336
Baie-Comeau	362
Timmins	352
Chicoutimi	345
Owen Sound	340
Charlottetown	339
Quebec	337
Sydney	330

**Cities With Lowest Annual
Average Snowfall**
(in centimetres)

Victoria	47
Vancouver	55
Penticton	73
Kamloops	86
Saskatoon	105
Brandon	106
Regina	107
Medicine Hat	108
Estevan	110
Winnipeg	115

Most Days Below Freezing
(average number of days
per year with freezing
temperatures)

Thompson	241
Yellowknife	225
Whitehorse	225
Prince Albert	216
Red Deer	212
Timmins	212
Fort McMurray	211
Val-d'Or	208
Edmonton	207
Brandon	205

Fewest Days Below Freezing
(fewest average number of
days per year with freezing
temperatures)

Vancouver	51
Victoria	58
Prince Rupert	97
Penticton	123
Windsor	130
St. Catharines	131
Kamloops	135
Sarnia	140
Belleville	142
Hamilton	145

Longest Frost-Free Period
(in days)

Vancouver	223
Victoria	202
Windsor	182

St. Catharines	174
Nanaimo	174
Hamilton	170
Sarnia	167
Belleville	165
Kingston	162
Montreal	158

Shortest Frost-Free Period
(in days)

Thompson	64
Whitehorse	76
Timmins	91
Fort McMurray	92
Prince George	93
Val-d'Or	94
Prince Albert	95
Sherbrooke	102
Red Deer	107
Thunder Bay	107

Wettest Cities
(total annual precipitation
in millimetres)

Prince Rupert	2,552
St. John's	1,482
Sydney	1,480
Halifax	1,474
Saint John	1,433
Moncton	1,229
Quebec	1,208
Charlottetown	1,201
Corner Brook	1,186
Vancouver	1,167

Driest Cities		Yellowknife	6
(most number of days without		Whitehorse	6
measurable precipitation)		Corner Brook	6
Medicine Hat	271	Sept-Iles	7
Lethbridge	265	Charlottetown	9
Kamloops	263	Sydney	9
Moose Jaw	260		
Brandon	258	**Sunshine Capitals**	
Saskatoon	257	(greatest number of hours	
Penticton	257	of sunshine per year)	
Regina	256	Estevan	2,500
Calgary	254	Medicine Hat	2,433
Swift Current	253	Moose Jaw	2,396
		Calgary	2,395
		Saskatoon	2,381
Most Thunderstorms		Brandon	2,380
(most days per year with		Winnipeg	2,377
thunderstorms)		Swift Current	2,375
London	36	Regina	2,365
Windsor	35	Yorkton	2,331
St. Catharines	31		
Kitchener	31		
Portage La Prairie	30	**Sunniest Winters**	
Toronto	28	(most hours of sunshine	
Winnipeg	28	during December, January	
Montreal	26	and February)	
Hamilton	26	Winnipeg	358
Edmonton	25	Calgary	353
		Estevan	349
Fewest Thunderstorms		Fredericton	348
(fewest days per year with		Thunder Bay	342
thunderstorms)		Saint John	338
Victoria	3	Halifax	336
Prince Rupert	3	Moose Jaw	323
St. John's	4	Saskatoon	322
Vancouver	6	Yorkton	321

Sunniest Summers

(most hours of sunshine during
June, July and August)

Yellowknife	1,037
Medicine Hat	957
Estevan	955
Swift Current	939
Regina	933
Moose Jaw	933
Lethbridge	924
Saskatoon	923
Winnipeg	898
Cranbrook	894

Blowing Snow

(greatest number of days per
year with blowing snow)

Chicoutimi	37
Regina	28
Moose Jaw	28
St. John's	27
Charlottetown	26
Swift Current	26
Portage La Prairie	25
Sault Ste Marie	25
Winnipeg	24
Owen Sound	24

Glaze Capitals

(greatest number of days
per year with freezing
precipitation)

St. John's	38
North Bay	20
Sydney	19

Sudbury	19
Charlottetown	17
Moncton	17
Ottawa–Hull	17
Val-d'Or	16
Halifax	16
Thompson	16

Foggiest Cities

(greatest number of days
per year with fog)

St. John's	121
Saint John	102
Halifax	101
Sydney	78
Sudbury	67
North Bay	62
Moncton	59
Prince George	57
Sept-Iles	53
London	49

Fog-Free Cities

(fewest number of days per
year with fog)

Penticton	2
Kamloops	8
Medicine Hat	10
Lethbridge	13
Kelowna	15
Whitehorse	15
Portage La Prairie	16
Winnipeg	17
Cranbrook	17
Edmonton	18

Most Humid Cities

(highest average vapour pressure, kPa, during June, July and August)

Windsor	1.78
Kingston	1.74
London	1.66
Kitchener	1.63
Montreal	1.61
Hamilton	1.61
Toronto	1.59
Owen Sound	1.54
Ottawa–Hull	1.53
Charlottetown	1.52

Windiest Cities

(greatest average annual wind speed in kilometres per hour)

St. John's	24
Swift Current	22
Sydney	20
Regina	20
Charlottetown	19
Lethbridge	19
Halifax	18
Saint John	18
Sudbury	18
Winnipeg	18

Clearest Skies

(annual number of hours per year with clear skies — between zero-tenths and two-tenths sky cover)

Estevan	2,979
Swift Current	2,740
Brandon	2,737
Winnipeg	2,706
Portage La Prairie	2,652
Yorkton	2,651
Regina	2,628
Moose Jaw	2,613
North Battleford	2,595
Prince Albert	2,512

Cloudiest Skies

(annual number of hours per year with overcast skies — between eight-tenths and ten-tenths sky cover)

Prince Rupert	6,123
St. John's	5,916
Chicoutimi	5,297
Prince George	5,258
Vancouver	5,240
Val-d'Or	5,142
Sydney	5,107
Halifax	5,075
Whitehorse	5,067
Owen Sound	4,980

ALBERTA'S CHINOOKS

A T MIDNIGHT ON JANUARY 27, 1962, THE TEMPERA-ture was −19°C at Pincher Creek, Alberta. Within an hour, it jumped 22 degrees as the winds swung around to the west-southwest gusting to 95 kilometres per hour. The snow cover disappeared like magic. While spectacular, the weather change was not unusual. Residents knew a "chinook" was under way and that the weather might continue spring-like for days, or revert just as suddenly to its previous wintry cold.

❄ On January 6, 1966, at Pincher Creek, Alberta, a chinook sent the temperature soaring 21°C in only four minutes.

Chinook is a native Canadian word meaning "snow eater." It was first used by a non-native Canadian in the 1860s to describe the *foehn*, a class of strong winds that become warm and dry as they flow down a mountain slope. A Hudson's Bay Company employee working in the Oregon Territory claimed that the occasional warm westerly wind always seemed to blow from a Chinook Indian encampment. According to tradition, the chinook is the warm breath of an Indian princess.

❄ Average number of days with chinook winds during the winter: Lethbridge, 35; Pincher Creek, 29; Calgary, 27; Medicine Hat, 24; Jasper, 14; Edmonton, 12; Banff, 10; and Lake Louise, 3.

In other mountainous regions of the world, the *foehn* (the name originated in the Alps) has a variety of names: *zonda* in Argentina, *koembang* in Java, and *puelche* in the Andes. The foehn winds are said to adversely affect human health. During the foehn, accident, crime and suicide rates are reported to rise in Germany.

Chinooks often occur over the western plains of North America but are at their greatest strength in southwestern Alberta, where they funnel through Crowsnest Pass and fan out across the southern part of the province, with diminishing effect as they cross into Saskatchewan. At Crowsnest Pass, chinooks occur an average of 30 days per winter, in Calgary it's 27; in Medicine Hat, 24; in Edmonton, 12; and in Swift Current, only 10.

❋ The cloud formation known as the Chinook Arch is a band of lenticular altocumulus cloud.

Lethbridge is the chinook capital of Canada with chinooks occurring an average of 35 days per winter. Although the city gets an average of 141 centimetres of snow each winter, it is unusual to have a snow cover of more than 25 centimetres; bare ground is the norm. On February 25, 1986, chinook winds gusted to 166 kilometres per hour in the Lethbridge area causing considerable damage. When 107 centimetres of snow on the ground melted in just eight hours, fields and pastures were turned into lakes.

Signalling the arrival of a chinook wind is an arch of low cloud in the western sky paralleling the Rockies. The wind always blows from the southwest or west and is strong (40 to 80 kilometres per hour) and gusty enough (up to 160 kilometres per hour) to lift roofs, snap power lines, shatter windows and even topple pedestrians. Rapid temperature rises and falls are classic and the air is desert dry.

When westerly winds carry warm, moist air from the Pacific, they first reach the Coast Mountains and glide up and over the western slopes. At higher elevations, the air expands and cools, about 1°C for every 200 metres of rise. In the ascent, the moisture in the air condenses and falls as rain or snow, and in the process great quantities of stored heat are released into the atmosphere. The process is repeated with

❋ Chinooks can occur year-round causing widespread soil erosion in the spring and fall and drying out crops in the summer.

❄ "It was so cold Christmas Eve (–47.8°C) in Winnipeg that upon retiring for the night I tried to blow out the candle, but the flame was frozen, so I just had to break it off."

From the 1879 memoirs of a log-cabin pioneer

each successive interior mountain chain traversed and with each ascent more moisture is "wrung" from the east-travelling air stream. Once over the final mountain barrier (the Rockies), dry air plunges to the plains, warming again by compression (like air warmed inside a bicycle pump) at a rate twice the cooling rate of the rise. Compression of the air coming into Alberta raises the temperature eight to 10 degrees above that of the Pacific air at the same elevation on the west side of the Coast Mountains.

To southern Albertans, a chinook is a mixed blessing. While most welcome temporary relief from the bitter cold of winter, a few are bothered by debilitating reactions ranging from sleeplessness to severe migraines. Others worry about decreased soil moisture, wind-blown topsoil and disrupted skiing conditions. But positive aspects also ensue, including natural snow removal and the exposure of forage for cattle and wildlife, not to mention golf in January and lilac blooms in February, however short-lived they may be.

AND MAY ALL YOUR CHRISTMASES BE WHITE

LONG BEFORE IRVING BERLIN COMPOSED "WHITE Christmas," snow on the ground Christmas morning was as important as turkey, tinsel and toys. Indeed, for most Canadians, Christmas celebrations are not the same on mornings when the landscape is a dreary brown or an emerald green.

For early North American pioneers, noting the colour of the ground cover on December 25 was thought to be helpful for forecasting weather conditions in the coming months. Among the popular Christmas weather proverbs are:

A green Christmas makes a heavy harvest.

At Christmas, meadows green;
At Easter, covered with frost.

The shepherd would rather see his wife enter the stable on Christmas Day than the sun.

If windy on Christmas Day, the trees will bear much fruit.

A warm Christmas, a cold Easter;
A green Christmas, a white Easter.

Christmas in mud, Easter in snow;
Christmas in snow, Easter in mud.

Thunder during Christmas week indicates there will be much snow during the winter.

If ice will bear a man at Christmas, it will not bear a mouse afterward.

To predict the likelihood of a white Christmas across Canada, we turn to

❄ Irving Berlin wrote "White Christmas" for the musical motion picture called *Holiday Inn.* "White Christmas" won the Oscar for the best song of 1942. It is the all-time favourite popular song for Christmas, having been recorded by no fewer than 400 artists. Bing Crosby's recording is the best-selling single record in history. When *Holiday Inn* was remade in 1954, the real star of the show was recognized and the film was renamed *White Christmas.*

❄ "On December 24th, there was a magnificent auororal display as we travelled along, consisting of streamers of all colours, which was so bright that it continued visible until it was quite light and the sun had almost risen. Towards daybreak the cold wind again sprung up. In the afternoon we reached Fort Edmonton just in time to join in the fun of Christmas Eve. This trip occupied 29 days; and the distance we walked, excluding side trips, was 536 miles."

From the papers of John Palliser's expedition, 1858.

weather records collected over the past 30 years. The accompanying map shows the chances of snow covering the ground to a depth of two centimetres or more sometime between Christmas Eve and Boxing Day.

Almost all of Quebec, Northern Ontario, the central and northern Prairies, the Arctic, Yukon and northern British Columbia can count on a white Christmas every year. In southern Ontario, six to eight out of 10 Christmases are white. There is a 40-percent chance along the Atlantic coast of Nova Scotia, and less than a 20-percent chance in the southwestern mainland of British Columbia and on Vancouver Island.

Those dreaming of a white Christmas might consider moving to Quebec City, Thunder Bay, Winnipeg or Saskatoon where there is a 100-percent chance that the ground will be white during the holiday season. Those four cities have had a perfect record for the past 30 years, but longtime residents of Winnipeg may remember the snow-free Christmas of 1939. As for other major cities, the likelihood of a white Christmas is as follows: Halifax, 48 percent; Montreal, 83 percent; Ottawa, 84 percent; Toronto, 63 percent; Regina, 94 percent; Calgary, 63 percent; Edmonton, 98 percent; and Vancouver, six percent.

This says nothing about the depth of snow — only that there would be two centimetres or more. Of the 100 towns and cities in this survey, Timmins, Ontario, had the deepest average snow cover on Christmas morning — 47 centimetres; Quebec City was close at 40 centimetres. For some southeastern cities, downtown locations have a slightly smaller chance of experiencing a white Christmas than suburban locations. For example, downtown Toronto has a 54-percent chance while Pearson International Airport, only 19 kilometres away, has a 63-percent chance. However, in Edmonton, both city and country airports are 98-percent sure of having a white Christmas.

Generally, Christmas has been greener for more Canadians on average over the last five years than at any time over the past 30 years. A trend? Another symptom of the greenhouse effect? No one knows for certain.

On Christmas morning 1983, people living in Eastern Canada, southern Alberta and southern British Columbia woke up to the most widespread green Christmas in 30

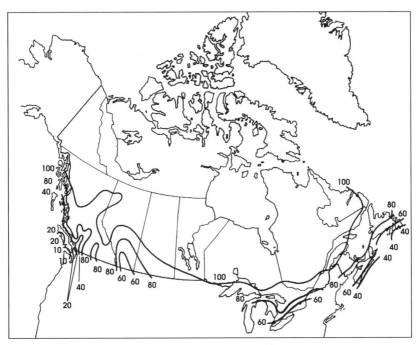

Percentage chance of a white Christmas.

years. On the other hand, in 1972, all of Canada was snow-covered during the holiday period. And the years 1971 and 1973 saw almost as much white from coast to coast.

Will your Christmas be white this year? Again, no one knows for sure. But if the record of the last 30 years holds true, Christmas should be white in Quebec City, Winnipeg, and in the North; green in Victoria and Vancouver; and it could go either way in Toronto, Halifax and St. John's.

Whatever the weather, may your Christmas be merry.

CHRISTMAS DAY SNOW COVER

City	Average Depth (cm)	Greatest Amount/ Year (cm)	Least Amount (cm)	Chance of a White Christmas (percent)
St. John's	12	51 1958	0	64
Charlottetown	19	89 1970	0	85
Halifax	10	64 1970	0	48
Fredericton	20	104 1970	0	87
Quebec City	40	91 1968	8	100
Montreal	15	51 1970	0	83
Ottawa	18	64 1970	trace	84
Toronto	5	20 1963	0	63
London	9	30 1963	0	75
Winnipeg	17	80 1955	2	100
Regina	14	36 1964	trace	94
Saskatoon	12	28 1961	5	100
Calgary	5	25 1955	0	63
Edmonton	16	43 1970	1	98
Vancouver	1	30 1964	0	6
Victoria	0.5	8 1971	0	5
Whitehorse	23	51 1971	5	100
Yellowknife	26	51 1957	5	100

SOME MEMORABLE CHRISTMAS WEATHER EVENTS IN CANADA

- **1872** Torontonians got a white Christmas, but not the one they were dreaming of. On the 25th and 26th, the city received 58.4 centimetres of snow, its greatest two-day snowfall on record. Gale-force winds caused massive drifts and combined with –16°C to –18°C temperatures to produce severe wind chill. The Great Western train from Hamilton was about 3½ hours late.

- **1968** Boxing Day marked the beginning of the snowiest and coldest spell at Victoria in 20 years. Almost 28 centimetres of snow fell on the last days of December, and over a five-week period, 120 centimetres of snow fell (the norm is 20 centimetres). The temperature bottomed at –15.6°C on the 29th, an all-time low, and the maximum temperature stayed below freezing for 11 consecutive days.

- **1970** At Turtle Creek, New Brunswick, a "Paul Bunyon" snowfall began on December 24. Five days later the snowfall accumulation was 125 centimetres.

- **1972** A Christmas Day rainstorm at Vancouver set an all-time 24-hour rainfall record; more than 50 weather stations in the Vancouver district recorded in excess of 100 millimetres during the storm.

- **1979** On the 25th, the 15,000-tonne *Lee Wang Zin* capsized 30 kilometres northeast of Rose Point in the Queen Charlotte Islands in gale-force winds and high seas. All crewmen were lost.

- **1980** Boxing Day floods near Vancouver caused $13 million in damage along the Squamish River. Residents were evacuated following a week of heavy rains and flooding. Hope recorded 444 millimetres of precipitation in December (178 percent of normal).

- **1980** A severely cold Christmas Day in Ontario and Quebec — temperatures were in the –25°C to –40°C range with strong winds. Two years later, it was the warmest Christmas Day ever across southern districts of central Canada. Toronto's 17.2°C was the warmest in 142 years of record-keeping.

- **1986** A severe ice storm struck the Ottawa Valley and southwestern Quebec on Christmas Eve. Fallen trees snapped hydro wires and damaged property. One home in four was without power on Christmas Day and many residents had to make alternative plans for Christmas dinner. Nearly 14 hours of freezing rain deposited about 30 millimetres of precipitation.

- **1991** A Christmas Day storm raced across Newfoundland bringing with it snow, rain, freezing rain and strong winds. Corner Brook recorded nearly 40 centimetres of snow. Heavy rains and freezing rain to the east caused flooding that forced some residents living in the Placentia Bay area to evacuate their homes.

SPRING FEVER IN JANUARY

JANUARY IS THE TIME FOR THE MIDWINTER BLAHS, WHEN cold, snow and ice seem to last forever. Even more disconcerting is knowing that plenty of winter is still to come — the year's coldest temperatures are still a month away and more than half of the season's snowfall has yet to be shovelled.

Then, right on cue around the middle of the month, a most welcome respite occurs in many parts of Canada. The thermometer climbs above freezing, often for the first time in weeks, the snow cover thins overnight, and the ice on sidewalks and outdoor rinks softens. Canadians are prematurely afflicted with spring fever, tossing off toques, unzipping parkas and forgetting that, officially, spring is at least 60 days away. The January thaw has arrived!

January thaw, or bonspiel thaw as it is called on the Prairies, is a climatic phenomenon of unseasonably warm weather that tends to arrive at about the same time every year, usually within 10 days of the middle of January. Generally, the thaw is gradual and temporary, lasting anywhere from a few hours to a week. Specifically, a pronounced thaw consists of at least two consecutive days with a maximum temperature of 2°C or more.

❄ The January thaw is a lifesaver for a great many animals. The melt compacts the snow, enabling animals to forage for food.

The arrival of the January thaw on the same date every year is no certainty, but the timing is sufficiently consistent that it has gained an honoured position in our weatherlore. ("A January spring is worth nothing." "Always expect a thaw in

January.") For winter-weary Canadians, no weather is perhaps more appreciated and better remembered than the January thaw. Indeed, so popular is the thaw that any winter mild spell is often referred to as the January thaw, even when it comes in December or February.

Although the midwinter upsurge in temperature appears consistent enough, the phenomenon is not recognized as real by meteorologists, who call it a "singularity." A singularity is an annual weather episode, usually an anomalous departure, that recurs at roughly the same time every year in a majority of years. It is not fully recognized as real because even the most pronounced singularity occurs in little more than half of all the years, although its frequency is greater than that expected by chance alone, and few plausible explanations can be advanced for its occurrence.

> ❄ Meteorologists call the January thaw a singularity because it occurs on or near a certain date with unusual regularity. Other singularities include Indian summer, old-wives summer, Christmas cyclone, and equinoctial gales in late September and March.

Other calendar-bound weather singularities include Indian summer in North America, and St. Luke's little summer in Europe; peak June rainfalls on the Prairies; the Christmas stormy period in eastern North America and in Europe; equinoctial gales in late September and late March; and ice saints (cold spells) in the first part of May in Europe.

The graph of daily winter temperature normals over 30 years for Ottawa is not unlike the rhythm of daily temperatures at other places in Canada. Most daily irregularities are smoothed out, revealing a normal seasonal progression; that is, an overall decline in temperature as winter advances to a low point in early to mid-February, and then a slow, consistent rise toward summer beginning sometime in February or March. Mild or cold spells

AVERAGE AFTERNOON TEMPERATURES (°C) FOR OTTAWA

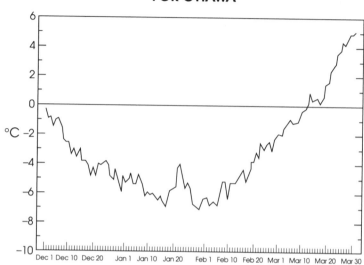

should appear randomly throughout the winter over 30 years so the likelihood of relatively mild or cold days would be roughly the same for any day. But such is not the case. In Ottawa, for example, the chance of a pronounced January thaw is three times greater in the period from January 21 to 27 than it is from January 7 to 13 or January 28 to February 3.

The accompanying table shows statistics on frequency of occurrence, duration and preferred times of the January thaw for several Canadian cities.

A pronounced January thaw does not happen every year; for example, only 22 percent of Januaries in Winnipeg, 41 percent in Regina and 75 percent in Ottawa experience such a thaw. If one accepts the definition of a thaw as any time an above-freezing temperature occurs in

AVERAGE JANUARY THAW CHARACTERISTICS
(based on 30 years of record)

City	Percent chance of one or more days above 0°C in January	Pronounced Thaw*
St. John's	100	98
Charlottetown	100	91
Halifax	100	100
Moncton	98	84
Montreal	96	83
Toronto	98	90
Ottawa	94	75
Winnipeg	58	22
Regina	82	41
Edmonton	94	81
Yellowknife	13	0
Whitehorse	79	51
Vancouver	100	100

City	Duration (days)	Favoured January Dates	Warmest Day in Thaw Period
St. John's	4	25–28	27
Charlottetown	3	21–28	26
Halifax	6	20–27	24
Moncton	4	22–28	26
Montreal	4	19–27	25
Toronto	5	20–26	22
Ottawa	3	19–26	22
Winnipeg	2	18–24	21
Regina	2	17–23	23
Edmonton	4	16–23	18
Yellowknife	1	17–24	18
Whitehorse	27	16–23	22
Vancouver	27	13–21	15

* At least two consecutive days with a maximum temperature of 2°C or more.

153

January, then the "thaw" is a certainty, at least in Eastern Canada. For example, Toronto only once in 150 Januaries has had no thaw period, whereas Halifax has never had a thawless January. On the other hand, Winnipeg experiences a January thaw in slightly more than half of the years, and a pronounced thaw in fewer than a quarter of them.

Perhaps most remarkable is that January thawing occurs later in the month as one travels eastward across Canada: from January 16 to 23 in Edmonton; 18 to 24 in Winnipeg; 19 to 27 in Montreal; 21 to 28 in Charlottetown; and 25 to 28 in St. John's. That eastward progression of warming during the third and fourth weeks is consistent with similar events in the United States. Significant thaws might typically last from two or three days to a week, but rarely longer. In Vancouver, it's a different story. Along the Pacific coast, they last a full month in most years. Another characteristic of the January thaw is its tendency to start gradually with an upsurge in temperature over several days, but to end with a relatively sudden drop to much below normal readings. Often accompanying the bitterly cold air are gale-force, northerly winds and a snowfall. More often than not, the end of the thaw heralds the arrival of the lowest temperatures of the winter.

Records for the last 100 years in Ottawa show that the date of the pronounced thaw has changed from earlier in the month at the beginning of the century to its present date around January 22. The frequency of significant thaws has increased slightly from about five to six per decade for the first 30 years of this century to about seven per decade in recent times. Climatologists attribute this to normal climate change, not to global warming.

What causes the January thaw is no mystery. General atmospheric circulation becomes more westerly, or even southwesterly, and mild Pacific air spreads eastward across

Canada. The stronger-than-normal westerlies in mid-latitudes tend to confine arctic air northward and favour the intrusion of warm, humid air from the subtropics into the eastern United States and Canada. Although the westerly flow may last several days, it inevitably shifts to northwesterly, again allowing outbreaks of arctic air to stream southward and eastward.

Still a mystery, though, is why this phenomenon occurs when it does. Is it just coincidence or is there a logical physical explanation? Some researchers offer statistical evidence for a relationship between January thaws and sunspot activity. Others attribute the warming spell to a readjustment of the atmosphere from an early-winter to a late-winter stage.

Whatever the explanation, this midwinter reprieve is one weather anomaly that should be enjoyed for as long as it lasts, for it never seems to last long enough.

ST. JOHN'S — CANADA'S WEATHER CHAMPION

S T. JOHN'S, NEWFOUNDLAND, HAS ONE OF THE TOUGH-est climates in Canada. Of all major Canadian cities, St. John's is the foggiest, snowiest, wettest, windiest and cloudiest. Furthermore, it has more days with freezing rain and wet weather than any other large city. While St. John's may be awash in negative weather superlatives, it also happens to have the third mildest winter — next to Victoria and Vancouver — in Canada. Because of its year-round temperate and equitable climate, St. John's can boast like its Pacific counterparts of having the greatest variety of trees and shrubs anywhere in Canada.

Shovelling out snowbound cars after a major snowstorm in St. John's, Newfoundland.

For residents of St. John's, weather is a frequent focus of complaints — late springs, summer wind chills, ice-blocked harbours, and seemingly endless overcast days. In many cases, their complaints are understandable. But in general, it might be more accurate to say that St. John's residents have a profound respect for, and immense interest in, the weather. How could it be otherwise, when in the span of one day it can present a terrifying hazard, a challenge, a threat, a disappointment and a pleasure?

Such qualities easily become the stuff of legend. Peter Morris, an information officer at Memorial University, compares weather in St. John's to a folk tune passed down from generation to generation. What has been passed down, though, is centuries of weather exaggeration. English merchants of the 1790s, bent on discouraging competition, spoke of Newfoundland as "a rock totally unsuited for human habitation . . . [a place that] suffers heavy mist, thick fog, dismal overcast and rain." But others wanted to promote early settlement, and their hyperbole would put today's most lavish travel brochure to shame: "great wealth of sunshine . . . fogs hundreds of miles from our coasts . . . the salubrity and mildness of the climate."

The truth is that St. John's is home to a fascinating array of weather. Perched on the continent's eastern tip, the city sits at the intersection of immense weather-generating systems. Its variability and moist, temperate salt air are what you would expect from a marine climate, but air masses from eastern North America also sweep over the city, bringing marked weather contrasts. St. John's has a

> ❄ Before July 1, bergy bits and growlers may be seen off the coast of St. John's. Bergy bits are remnants of large icebergs, which are still visible above the sea. Growlers are small remnants of icebergs, which are almost entirely submerged beneath the ice, but which cause considerable damage to ships when dashed by heavy waves.

❄ On July 9, 1981, an Air Canada 727 with 90 persons aboard was struck by lightning as it took off from St. John's. No injuries were reported.

deserved reputation as one of the stormiest areas on the continent.

Fog, snow, wind and freezing rain make the airport one of the most difficult in Canada for take-offs and landings. The airport lacks the city's buffer of hills to shield it against the worst weather from the ocean, 10 kilometres away, so weather data for the airport and the city often diverge; the airport is prone to stronger winds, cooler temperatures, and more snow and freezing precipitation. As for fog, locals are quick to point out that when the airport is fogged in, the city may be basking in bright sunshine or merely lying under a low cloud base.

Despite their ferocious reputations, winters in St. John's are comparatively mild. That knowledge may be little consolation when one of the frequent, strong northwesterly winds wraps the city in a sudden surge of cold air. Still, it helps to know that the next influx of moist, mild air is never far away over the Atlantic Ocean.

Winter temperatures seem to oscillate at the freezing mark. The mildness and rains, combined with heavy snowfalls, make for sloppy, slushy weather. Two or three times every winter, an Atlantic storm dumps an enormous snowfall on St. John's and buffets the city with powerful winds.

January and February 1987 have gone down in the record books as the snowiest beginning to a year in recent memory, made worse by the absence of the usual thawing between snowstorms. Altogether, in excess of 241 centimetres (almost eight feet) of snow fell, more than 100 centimetres above normal. A snow-laden section of roof collapsed at a St. John's shopping mall, injuring seven people. City residents who could not open their doors had to climb out second-storey windows. Many side streets remained closed or with only a single path through them until March.

In general, though, nature often aids by melting the snow. The city can normally expect its first snowfall by mid-November, and flurries as late as early May, while the season for persistent snow cover lasts about 110 days from mid-December to early April.

Freezing rain, known locally as "silver thaw," is another major weather hazard of winter and early spring in St. John's. One of the worst to strike the city began on the evening of April 11, 1984, and continued intermittently for 60 hours. Jackets of ice as much as 15 centimetres thick weighed down electrical power lines, freezing them together in networks of silver spider webs. Electrical power interruptions left 200,000 people in the Avalon Peninsula without heat and light for days. In some parts of St. John's, cooking a hot meal meant priming camp stoves or firing up barbecues. The only bargain in town was fresh meat: freezers had no power, and the meat had to be sold quickly. Customers stood in line for hours at retail stores to buy kerosene heaters and cooking fuel, and at restaurants to order a hot meal.

St John's may have the same latitude as Paris, but a "springtime in Paris" it is not! Rather than stroll the open cafés of Water Street, "townies" — as St. John's residents are known — are more apt to count icebergs, shovel snow, brace themselves against arctic chills, and hide from a nor'easter. Little wonder that Colin Banfield, geography professor at Memorial University and a 20-year resident of St. John's, says it is difficult to find anyone who will praise the city's spring weather, which is slow to arrive in the best of years. Pack ice may linger until May or early June, and icebergs sometimes remain close offshore into August.

As a result, onshore winds bring spells of fog, overcast and drizzle. Even when the sun shines, it's never very warm.

St. John's has a reputation for being enshrouded in perpetual fog from April through August, which is not entirely deserved. True, the nearby ocean waters are among the foggiest in the world. Bands of thick, cool fog lie off the coast, generated where the chilled air above the Labrador Current mixes with the warm, moisture-laden air above the Gulf Stream. Indeed, across the northern Grand Banks in an average July, fog dense enough to restrict visibility to less than one kilometre is present 52 percent of the time. But at St. John's Airport, such low visibility occurs only 10 percent of the time in July, and less often in the city. An interesting aspect of Newfoundland fog is that it is often accompanied by strong winds. Normally, winds can be expected to dissipate fog, but here the fog is frequently so thick and widespread that the winds have little clearing effect.

Newfoundland has the strongest winds of any province and St. John's has the strongest winds of any major city. Winds blow predominantly from the west in winter and west-southwest in summer, although topography tends to modify the direction and speed to some degree. Northeasterlies are the most dreaded because they are often accompanied by rain, freezing drizzle and snow — and sometimes all three at the same time. The combination of low temperatures and strong winds can produce severe wind chill that inhibits outdoor activity. However, the marine effect causes a moderating influence on winter wind chill values. It also produces uncomfortable summer wind chills on occasion.

Although summers in St. John's are short and cool by southern Canadian standards, summer days there are among the most delightful anywhere. With afternoon highs in the low 20s, they are warm enough to be comfortable and yet cool enough to permit vigorous outdoor work or play. Other summer bonuses are low levels of humidity and haze, few thunderstorms, rarely any hail, and never a tornado. August is usually warmer than July, reflecting the slow warming release of the surrounding ocean, but extremes seldom exceed 30°C more than twice a year. The summer of 1984 was almost perfect — clear blue skies and record high sunshine, with little rainfall and mild temperatures. But not every summer is so agreeable; it snowed in July 1949, the year Newfoundland became Canada's tenth province. Also, St. John's may occasionally miss summer almost entirely, as it did in cold, foggy 1991 and 1992.

Autumn is the favourite season for many townies. St. John's, and Newfoundland generally, is blessed with some of the finest Indian summers anywhere — warm, cloudless days under an azure sky. Fall temperatures are relatively mild owing to the warmth from the ocean. Frosts are delayed until mid-October most years, and no lasting snow cover appears until well into December. The occasional rude surprise comes from a close brush with a dying hurricane moving up the eastern seaboard, but its power is quickly dispelled by cold northern waters.

Whatever the weather, St. John's is a great outdoor city with much to do. It may be ringing in the New Year at the harbourfront, fly fishing for brown trout in the Reflecting Pond, cheering the racers on Regatta Day on Quidi Vidi Lake, or watching ships in the landlocked harbour — when the weather co-operates, residents of St. John's proudly say there's no better place to be.

❄ On September 9, 1775, the "Independence Hurricane" struck the Atlantic Region with full force. About 4,000 sailors, mostly from the British Isles, were reported drowned. In St. John's, the storm tore roofs off some buildings and flattened others.

ST. JOHN'S WEATHER CAPSULE*

Temperature (°C)

	Summer	Winter
average midafternoon	20°	−1°
average early morning	11°	−8°
all-time high	32°	16°
all-time low	−3°	−24°

Precipitation

annual rainfall (mm)	1,163
annual snowfall (cm)	322

Average Annual Number of Days

fog	121
thunderstorms	4
rain	161
snow	87
freezing precipitation	38
frost	176

Sunshine

average annual total (hours)	1,527

Wind

	Summer	Winter
average speed (kilometres per hour)/ prevailing direction	22 WSW	27W
extreme gust (kilometres per hour)	122	193

Probability Data

chance of January thaw	100 percent
chance of white Christmas	64 percent
chance of groundhog seeing his shadow	53 percent
chance of a May snowfall	79 percent

* Data from St. John's (Torbay) Airport, 1990; conditions may vary in the city.

WHERE THE SUN SHINES BRIGHTEST

TRAVEL ADS, RESORT BROCHURES AND CHAMBERS OF Commerce often boast about abundant sunshine. The fact is, however, determining what place has the sunniest weather depends largely on how you express it. The sunniest day, month, summer or year on average? Or on record? The longest string or the greatest number of sunny days?

Eureka on Ellesmere Island, which is about as far north as you can go in Canada, holds the record for the most monthly sunshine ever recorded anywhere in Canada — 621 hours in May 1973, which averages to about 20 hours a day. Ah, you say, there would be precious little sun there in December. True. And so the 10,000-plus residents of Estevan in southern Saskatchewan can claim to live in the only place in Canada that receives at least 100 hours of sunshine in every month of the year. Even more impressive, Estevanites can brag that they have the greatest number of sunshine hours — 2,500 — of any place in Canada in an average year, and this is the most commonly accepted indicator of the sunniest place.

> ❄ The sunniest place in the world is the eastern Sahara desert with an average annual sunshine duration of 4,300 hours.

Calgary can make the same claim for cities with over 100,000 people, and Coronation, Alberta, for towns with less than 10,000. Not to be left in the dark, Winnipeg can exult in being the sunniest provincial capital. Residents of Manyberries, Alberta, are not impressed. Their town

163

holds the record for the sunniest year — 2,785 sunshine hours in 1976. Moreover, Manyberries has the longest unbroken string of days with some sunshine — 254. Harrow, Ontario, near Windsor in Canada's "sun-parlour" and about as far south as you can go in the country, ranks second in this category with 219 days.

Try telling Maritimers that cloud and fog make their region the dullest place in Canada, and they'll retort with statistics to prove that New Brunswick is the sunniest province in all of Canada in December, and that Prince Edward Island has, on average, the shortest spell of consecutive days without sunshine — only ten.

If "sunniest" means the greatest number of sunny hours in summer, Yellowknife is first by far, with a three-month total of 1,037 hours or an average of 11 hours, 35 minutes a day. Yellowknife also has the sunniest summer month on average — July at 382 hours.

Other places beaming a sunny distinction: Winnipeg, Manitoba, with the sunniest winter on average; Vauxhall, Alberta, with more sunny days a year — 330 — on average (Calgary and Lethbridge tied for second with 329 days); and Medicine Hat, where in 1976 every day but 19 had at least a few minutes of sunshine.

❄ At 49° north latitude the longest day of the year, from sunrise to sunset, is 16 hours and 13 minutes and occurs about June 21; at the same latitude, the shortest day of the year, about December 21, has 8 hours and 13 minutes of daylight.

Quebec has more sites officially recording sunshine than any other province — 85 stations of the 300 in Canada. And Montrealers have a sunshine distinction of sorts, having had the only baseball game in major league history delayed due to glare. On July 1, 1974, the plate umpire was having trouble seeing and held up the start of the

game by 20 minutes. Newfoundland and British Columbia may not own any sunshine records, but both have a
place named Sunnyside.

All places on the earth receive approximately the same
daylight per year: about 4,380 hours. Hours of sunshine,
though, are much less because of cloud, mist, fog and hilly
terrain. The sunniest place in the world is the eastern
Sahara where 4,300 hours of sunshine, or 97 percent of
the possible amount, occur in an average year. Canada's
yearly average sunshine total of 1,950 hours is only

SUNNIEST PLACES IN CANADA

Sunniest month (hours)	Eureka, Northwest Territories (May 1973)	621
Greatest average annual number of sunny hours	Estevan, Saskatchewan	2,500
Major city with greatest annual average number of sunny hours	Calgary, Alberta	2,395
Sunniest small town under 10,000 population	Coronation, Alberta	2,450
Sunniest provincial capital	Winnipeg, Manitoba	2,377
Sunniest year on record	Manyberries, Alberta (1976)	2,785
Shortest spell of consecutive days without sun	Charlottetown, Prince Edward Island	10
Sunniest summer on average (hours)	Yellowknife, Northwest Territories	1,037
Sunniest winter on average (hours)	Winnipeg	358
Greatest annual number of hours of possible sunshine	Alert, Northwest Territories	4,580
Greatest annual average number of sunny days	Vauxhall, Alberta	330
Greatest number of sunny days in one year	Medicine Hat, Alberta (1976)	346

44 percent of possible. ("Possible" refers to the maximum duration of sunshine that would be observed for that location if the terrain were level, no obstructions existed and the sky were clear.) Canada's sunniest region in southern Saskatchewan has about 2,500 hours, or 57 percent of possible, comparable with Rome's but above Tokyo's (2,021 hours, or 45 percent) and less than Jerusalem's (3,474, or 78 percent) and Athens's (2,758, or 62 percent).

Without a doubt, the Prairies are the sunniest region in Canada, and the province there with the most sunshine is Saskatchewan. Province-wide, Saskatchewan averages about 50 hours more sunshine annually than Alberta, and has slightly more sunny hours than her western neighbour in both winter and summer. Only slightly less sunny is central British Columbia, the remaining prairie regions and southern Ontario. Despite the heavy rainfall, most of the Maritimes enjoy about 1,800 sunshine hours a year. The lowest averages are along the Pacific coast just south of the Alaska Panhandle, where the range is from 1,200 to 1,400 hours per year, and over the foggy parts of Newfoundland where fewer than 1,500 hours occur.

July is usually the sunniest month and December the dullest. April is sunnier than October, and in a few places, especially in the north, May is sunnier than June. In midsummer, most of southern Canada receives over 250 sunshine hours a month, about 60 percent of the possible amount, for an average of eight hours, 15 minutes a day. Again, the longest duration of sunshine on average (more than 340 hours a month) occurs over the southern Prairies, and the lowest along the northern British Columbia coast, a gloomy 140 hours, or four hours, 30 minutes a day. In winter, cloudy weather and the lack of sunshine are common across the country but are most pronounced along the northwest Pacific coast. Prince Rupert, for example, records clear skies only 15 percent of the time in December, for an average of 32 hours of sunshine.

In Canada, the standard bright-sunshine instrument is the Campbell–Stokes recorder, which was first developed in 1868. The principle involved in recording sunshine with this instrument is similar to burning paper by focusing sunshine with a hand-held magnifying glass. The recorder consists of a glass sphere 10 centimetres in diameter, supported in a curved metal bracket set on a pedestal. The instrument is situated away from nearby buildings and trees to prevent shading. The sun's rays are focused by the sphere on specially prepared paper cards, leaving a scorch mark or charred thin slit for those portions of the day when

ANNUAL AVERAGE SUNSHINE TOTALS (HOURS) FROM AROUND THE WORLD

Alice Springs	3,592	Naples	2,396
Athens	2,758	Nice	2,775
Barcelona	2,487	Paris	1,992
Buffalo	2,372	Phoenix	3,809
Charlottetown	1,844	Quebec City	1,910
Eastern Sahara	4,300	Regina	2,266
Edmonton	2,203	Rome	2,491
Fredericton	1,929	St. John's	1,527
Geneva	1,979	San Diego	2,982
Halifax	1,949	San Juan	3,592
Honolulu	3,067	Tampa	2,949
Jerusalem	3,474	Tokyo	2,021
Las Vegas	3,810	Toronto	2,038
Madrid	2,871	Victoria	2,082
Miami	2,945	Whitehorse	1,852
Moscow	1,597	Winnipeg	2,377

the sun is shining brightly. The rotation of the earth causes the burn to move along the card. Thus, by measuring the length of the burn, one knows how long the sun was shining.

Bright sunshine is not the same as visible sunshine. This is because the Campbell–Stokes instrument does not record sunshine until about half an hour after sunrise, and often about half an hour before sunset. At these times, the sun is only five degrees or less above the horizon and its intensity is not sufficient to burn the paper. Also, thin high cloud or heavy haze is a sufficient obstruction to prevent a burn on the card. The charts are changed daily and the charring is measured and recorded in tenths of hours. The total duration of bright sunshine for a month is the sum of the daily burn durations.

WEATHER
OBSERVERS

WEATHER WATCHERS FROM COAST TO COAST

IN 1933, AS A 16-YEAR-OLD FARM BOY IN RANFURLY, Alberta, Tom Waite had one extra chore each day. At 8 a.m. and again at 8 p.m., he would walk 30 metres behind the farmhouse to observe the weather. Fifty-five years (or 20,000 days) later, he is still walking the 30 metres twice a day to record the maximum and minimum temperatures and the amount of rain or snow.

Tom Waite is a member of Environment Canada's nation-wide network of 2,000 unpaid weather observers who record the temperature and precipitation every day of the year. Volunteers are of all ages and walks of life— farmers, homemakers, teachers, dentists, bankers, writers, pensioners, even prisoners. There is at least one mayor, a monk, an optometrist, a father of an MP, and a devotee to the Hare Krishna. Many weather stations are manned by individuals; others are operated by schools, power companies, agricultural experimental stations, industrial firms and municipalities. Some share the task with their spouses or members of their family, or with friends and neighbours.

While they are as different as individuals can be, all volunteers share a consuming interest in the weather: to them, watching the sky is a hobby like stamp collecting and needlepoint. Their motivation for years of dedication and unselfish service is simply the satisfaction of contributing to the community and to the nation. Environment Canada supplies and maintains the equipment for the observers and covers postage and other operating costs. Only in rare

❄ On September 6, 1840, the first official weather observation was made in Canada on the grounds of King's College, University of Toronto, by the British Royal Artillery.

cases is an observer paid, usually because Environment Canada is anxious for reports from a remote area where no willing observer can be found. In such cases, the payment is small.

The routine of a weather observer rarely varies. Twice a day the volunteer reads two thermometers — a maximum and a minimum — recording the temperature extremes that have occurred since the last observation. The thermometers are housed in a white louvred box, resembling a beehive, known as a Stevenson screen. (It was designed by Thomas Stevenson, a lighthouse engineer and father of author Robert Louis Stevenson.) A rain gauge sits on the ground nearby. The observer measures any rain collected since the last observation, then empties the gauge. The depth of freshly fallen snow is also measured. Notes regarding the character of the weather during the day — light snow, dense fog, sunny, or incidental remarks such as "spotted my first blue jay today" — are recorded. Some observers also measure elements like bright sunshine and wind speed.

❊ From what vocation are most volunteer weather observers recruited? (a) public servants; (b) teachers; (c) homemakers; (d) farmers. Answer: (d)

Observers usually arrange for replacements when they are ill or on holiday, so that the weather records from each site will continue without interruption. Someone is usually glad to stand in. At the end of each month, the observer mails a report to a regional office of Environment Canada. There the reports are verified, then sent to Environment Canada's Atmospheric Environment Service in Downsview, Ontario, where they are scrutinized again, processed and stored as a permanent record of Canada's climate.

Today's volunteers continue a long tradition of weather watching begun more than 200 years ago, long before a

❄ Each and every day around the world there are more than 100,000 weather observations taken from 9,000 stations in cities and at airports, 7,000 ships, and 1,000 upper-atmosphere stations. In addition, seven satellites provide pictures of weather systems.

national meteorological service existed in Canada. Missionaries, traders, Hudson's Bay Company factors, and explorers such as Henry Kelsey, David Thompson and John Palliser were among the early observers.

The first systematic weather observations in Canada began in 1742 when Jean-François Gaultier, king's physician of New France, kept a diary of daily weather for 14 years at Quebec City, about the time Benjamin Franklin was tracking a hurricane along the Atlantic coast using a network of observers. Weather journals were kept by the Reverend Charles Dade in Toronto during the 1830s, and by Dr. Charles Small-wood near Montreal in the 1850s. Between 1855 and 1880, the headmasters at about ten Upper Canada senior county grammar schools took thrice-daily observations.

Canada's weather network has spread across the country primarily because of volunteer efforts. Observing sites have grown from 126 in 1871 to more than 2,500 today. Weather volunteers come from every age group and occupation. One observer confined to a wheelchair on her Saskatchewan wheat farm observes storm clouds from her living room window and operates a ham radio. Another observer from Quebec rigged up teletype equipment in his home to receive weather reports and placed an anemometer on the roof to record wind speeds.

Weather-watching duties have often been passed down from one generation to another. Tom Waite's grandfather began recording the weather at Ranfurly in 1905, the year Alberta joined Confederation, and the Bairds of Brucefield, Ontario, have been weather observers at the same site since 1903.

Weather records, like antiques or good wine, tend to become more valuable with age. Although not used in forecasting, the records from these volunteer observers provide basic facts about Canada's climate. From them, statistics are compiled and applied; for example, in designing water and energy projects, settling insurance claims, and selecting sites for retirement communities. Each year Environment Canada responds to nearly 200,000 requests for climate information, which comes largely from the volunteer weather network. At times volunteers also provide knowledgeable advice on local climate within their communities by writing stories for weekly newspapers, or assisting regional offices in flood forecasting, pin-pointing the location of severe weather, or verifying some weather forecasts.

❋ Canada's oldest weather observer, Vernon Tuck, operated a weather station in his backyard until his retirement at the age of 92.

There are also weather volunteers aboard merchant and research ships. Back in 1947 only a dozen vessels on both coasts and the Great Lakes were taking weather observations. Today more than 300 vessels are involved in this activity.

Another corps of volunteers identifies and reports potentially hazardous weather. Thousands of severe-weather watchers from Alberta to Quebec maintain a sky watch for signs of hail, tornadoes, damaging winds or heavy precipitation, relaying sightings to a weather office by telephone. This simple task is vital for providing advance warning of dangerous conditions. Additional observers and severe-weather watchers are still needed in some parts of Canada. To join the volunteer program, contact the nearest Environment Canada weather office.

Canada's weather service is one of the few federal organizations with more volunteers than paid employees. It is

INSTRUMENTS FOR MEASURING WEATHER		
Weather	**Instrument**	**Units**
atmospheric pressure	barometer	kilopascals
temperature	thermometer	°C
rainfall	rain gauge	millimetres
snowfall	ruler/snow gauge	centimetres
sunshine	Campbell-Stokes recorder	hours
wind speed	anemometer	kilometres per hour
wind direction	wind vane	N E S W
humidity	wet-bulb thermometer	°C/percent

nice to know that in this automated world, these "back-yard" volunteers with their simple instruments are still such an important source of information.

CHRISTMAS WEATHER FROM THE TOP OF THE WORLD

AS THE SPIRIT OF CHRISTMAS CREEPS UNFAILINGLY through most Canadian households, conjuring up its cornucopia of delights in the imaginations of young and old, a thought might be spared for a small group of weather technicians locked away in a cheerless wasteland above the Arctic Circle. Sugar plums may be dancing in the heads of southerners, but isolation and mind-numbing cold are more likely in the thoughts of four intrepid observers braving the season away from family and friends in a tiny outpost 720 kilometres from the North Pole.

This is Alert, Northwest Territories, home to the "frozen chosen" who gather weather data, regardless of the season, in the starkness of the world's most northerly permanent settlement.

That they are not alone at the top of the world is probably cold comfort. Canada maintains about 30 other stations north of the Arctic Circle; the United States also has some, as does Russia, Iceland, Denmark (in Greenland), Finland, Norway and Sweden. None, however, is perched as far north as the Alert facility. Moreover, the weather centre is part of Canadian Forces Station Alert, established in 1956, where 200 military personnel live and work. It is Canada's most classified military station, a listening post for radio signals from around the world. Alert in winter has the look of a space station — a barren, remote, secret site ringed with radio antennae, locked in the grip of unspeakable cold and cloaked in near-perpetual darkness.

The weather station was built as part of a Canadian–American project in April 1950. Other high-arctic stations had preceded it at Resolute and Eureka in 1947, and Isachsen and Mould Bay in 1948. A phased withdrawal of United States support from the joint arctic weather stations began in 1970. Isachsen was closed in 1978.

Alert was named after one of the ships of the 1875–76 expedition by Sir George Strong Nares to survey the north coast of Ellesmere Island. Before an airstrip was built at Alert, equipment and supplies had to be shipped by icebreaker, or flown in from Thule in western Greenland and dropped by parachute. During one airlift in 1950, a Royal Canadian Air Force Lancaster crashed at

> ❄ All-time high at Alert: 20°C on July 8, 1956.
>
> ❄ All-time low at Alert: –50°C on February 9, 1979.

the weather station, killing all nine persons on board. A memorial cairn and nine crosses mark the grave site overlooking the Arctic Ocean.

Another tragedy occurred on October 30, 1991. A Canadian Forces C-130 Hercules on a resupply mission from Thule, Greenland, crashed on its final approach to the runway at Alert. Five of the 18 people on board died within 36 hours of the crash from injuries and hypothermia. Poor weather conditions hampered rescue operations: –60°C wind chill (cold enough to freeze exposed skin in one minute), 45-kilometre-per-hour winds, near-zero visibility in blowing snow, and overcast skies. It took almost two days through snow-bound ravines and in whiteout conditions for rescuers to reach the crash site.

Alert is not Canada's coldest weather station. That distinction belongs to Eureka, 400 kilometres to the southwest. Alert's average temperature is –18.2°C. Never on record has the temperature dipped below –50°C or risen above 20°C. There has never been a January thaw, and the average frost-free season lasts only four days.

❄ Greatest amount of snow on the ground: 89 centimetres on June 4, 1956.

The most memorable cold spell at Alert occurred in February 1979, the coldest month on record. Only once did the average temperature climb above –40°C. Meteorological technician Andrew Smart remembers cheering on February 9 when the thermometer registered –50°C, the lowest temperature ever recorded at the station. (It has been that cold in Regina, and even colder in Banff and Lake Louise.) Seasoned staff at Alert, though, are not unduly affected by periods of prolonged cold. For them a jump in temperature from –40°C to –20°C can feel like a spring day. Long winter walks under a full moon are often possible, the worry of becoming lost never a concern since a person's trail is always well marked by small clouds of ice crystals from his or her breath that hover at head level for some time afterwards. The total absence of strong winds make outdoor activities possible, although extra precautions must be taken to prevent throat and

> ❄ Longest string of days with maximum temperature below 0°C: 293 in 1956–7.

lung burn from overexertion in the frigid air. On the coldest days, station dogs burrow into the snow banks to insulate themselves against too rapid a heat loss.

Spring is the most welcome season. After months of darkness in below-freezing temperatures, skies lighten, the winds slacken and the air warms. Summer arrives slowly, but doesn't last long. With continuous daylight, however, there is time for building, repairing, cleaning, and playing baseball and golf — even around the clock. Although an exceptionally hot summer's day may bring double-digit temperatures, occasional snow showers remind Alertans where they are.

The High Arctic is one of the driest regions in the world, even though moisture is plentiful in its lakes and rivers, in the muskeg and permafrost, in the snow cover, in the permanent ice and in the Arctic Sea. Snowfall is surprisingly light, averaging 150 centimetres a year at Alert, about the same amount that Calgary gets and half that of Charlottetown. September is the snowiest month with an average of 12 snow days and an accumulation of 33 centimetres. Records show that there has never been a thunderstorm, and the average rainfall is a paltry 18 millimetres a year.

The contrast between the winter and summer versions of midnight above the Arctic Circle is not normally as great as southerners expect it to be, but it still holds a fascination for newcomers. Even at its lowest point in the sky on June 21, the midnight sun remains above the horizon, softly lighting up the night sky. On December 21, usually the shortest day of the year, polar night is seldom pitch black. A surprising amount of reflected sky light, moonlight and occasional northern lights (viewed by looking south) illuminate the ice-and-snow landscape from horizon to horizon.

At Alert, total dark or total daylight periods last about 21 weeks. On February 28, the sun makes its first appearance on the southern horizon, without question the most-heralded occasion of an arctic winter and the start of a celebration at the weather station that residents call the Sunrise Festival. In March, daylight increases by more than 15 minutes a day, with complete daylight beginning early in April. On October 15, the sun disappears for the winter.

❄ Highest wind chill reading was 2950 on January 6, 1958, with a temperature of –40.6°C and wind speed of 58 km/h.

Weather technicians at Alert, men and women usually in their twenties who are employees of Environment Canada, are posted for three to eight months. They receive at least three weeks' leave during that time. The daily work schedule consists of 10-hour shifts, and includes weather reporting every three hours and weather balloon releases every 12 hours. As well, there are weekly ice-thickness surveys at two locations, twice monthly snow surveys and daily radiation measurements.

A significant new program was begun at Alert in August 1986 with the opening of the world's most northerly environmental monitoring laboratory. Alert is now one of 20 global air-pollution observatories measuring greenhouse gases, such as carbon dioxide and methane, and arctic haze. Unfortunately, even on a clear day, you can no longer see forever in the Arctic, owing primarily to industrial pollution — soot particles, heavy metals, and organic and acidic sulphates — originating in

Europe and Russia. The remoteness of Alert ensures that if pollutants are present in the air there, they represent a contribution to global background pollution. The new laboratory also helps scientists identify major routes of toxic substances in the Arctic. For 20 years pesticides have been found in the snow on Ellesmere Island, in the air at Mould Bay, and in the internal organs of fish, seals, whales and polar bears.

Why do weather technicians come to this far end of the earth? For many, it is the money; generally, they work 55 hours a week, which, combined with overtime and isolation pay, can double their salary. Just the same, life is far from dull. The Arctic is no longer the dreaded, alien place of years gone by. Living at the top of the world is peaceful and silent, with most of the comforts of home provided. Other inducements include, on occasion, arctic cuisine (char, caribou and muskox), no heat waves, few pests, the possibility of seeing arctic wolves stalking muskoxen, dancing arctic hares, first-rate star gazing, and the chance to walk where few have ever gone.

The weather observers are lodged with the National Defence staff in one of three, large, two-storey buildings. The barracks are arranged in wings connected by a central corridor to the main complex, which has a dining room, post office, movie theatre, darkroom, library, television and ham radio studios, three bars and a commissary. Bedrooms are comfortable single accommodations, each furnished with a desk, chairs, a closet, dressers and a wash basin/vanity. All the modern conveniences are available, including running water and flush toilets. A medic and nurse provide health care.

Recreation may be the best in the Arctic, although, because of its position below the line of sight towards the geostationary satellite located above the equator, satellite signals cannot be received at Alert. Thus, all television programming (three channels operating non-stop) is canned, brought in from the south one or two weeks late. There is an FM-stereo radio station with volunteers playing music around the clock. A full-size gym includes a well-equipped exercise room. Attached to the gym are a two-lane bowling alley and a curling rink with two sheets of artificial ice. Photography, art, music, conversation and reading are popular hobbies. For about four weeks in summer, there is a small lake southwest of the station that is chock full of pan-sized arctic char for those who enjoy fishing.

Although weather observers at Alert are better off than most of their counterparts at other arctic stations, thanks to weekly incoming flights bearing mail and fresh produce, direct contact with family and friends in the south is limited, even at Christmas. The technicians are allowed only a 20-minute call home every eight to 10 days. Visitors and pets are not permitted. Christmas can therefore be a difficult time for the Alert staff. So spare a thought for them at Christmastime as they maintain their icy, isolated vigil.

CHRISTMAS DAY WEATHER AT ALERT		
	°C/cm	Year
Warmest temperature	−11.7°C	1970
Coldest temperature	−41.1°C	1950
Greatest snowfall	3.6 cm	1984
Deepest snow on ground	60 cm	1955
Least snow on ground	13 cm	1965, 1983

Ice-harvesting on Toronto's harbourfront in the days when the bay froze solid. ONTARIO ARCHIVES

LARGE CITIES CREATE THEIR OWN WEATHER

AT MIDNIGHT ON SEPTEMBER 6, 1840, LIEUTENANT Charles Riddell of the British Royal Artillery recorded the weather outside a newly built log observatory on the grounds of King's College, now the University of Toronto. It was clear, he wrote in his journal, with no wind or rain, and the temperature was a cool 52°F (11°C). This event heralded the recording of weather in Canada on a continuous, day-to-day basis.

❄ An energy tip from Ontario Hydro: To keep house heat in, plant coniferous trees on the north side to provide shelter from northerly winds. For summer cooling, plant deciduous trees on the east, west and south sides of the house.

Of course, casual weather observations were made sporadically by explorers, trappers, Hudson's Bay Company factors and missionaries for over three centuries. In Toronto, fragmentary weather records were taken in 1801 and 1820, and during the 1830s, the Reverend Charles Dade, headmaster of Upper Canada College, took weather observations two or three times a day. But none of these were continuous and for long enough periods to give a detailed picture of the climate.

Riddell had been posted to Canada in 1839 to set up an experimental meteorological and magnetic observatory on St. Helen's Island in Montreal but soon moved to Toronto. Quarters were obtained on the lakeshore at Fort York, where he began observing the weather on an irregular basis at the close of that year. At the same time, he looked for a more permanent site on higher, less swampy ground and away from the magnetic interference of the artillery and muskets, as well as from the noise of the barracks. By September 6, Riddell and three observers had moved to the new college observatory on two acres of land on the northwest outskirts of Toronto and begun their daily weather readings and other scientific observations. What started as a single weather station in 1840, grew to 126 in 1871, when the Canadian weather service was founded, and to more than 2,500 climate stations today.

❄ Human bodies in a room can be a significant source of heat. At rest each person gives off the heat equivalent of a 74-watt light bulb.

On September 5, 1990, when Jiri Werner, a technician with the University of Toronto geography department, walked to the weather instrument compound outside Trinity College and recorded the

afternoon temperature and the day's rainfall, it marked
the completion of a century and a half of continuous
weather observing in downtown Toronto.

This 150-year-old record is unparalleled in Canadian
meteorological history, with nearly 55,000 days of consecutive observations. The present weather station is
within sight of the original wooden observatory; six
moves of the weather site have taken place over the
years, each within one kilometre of each other. The
observations have always been taken at a height of about
one metre above the ground. The greatest environmental change has been the growth in Toronto, from a small
town of 13,000 people in 1840 to a vast industrial and
commercial metropolis exceeding three million people
today.

The foresight of our ancestors in observing the weather

AVERAGE ANNUAL TEMPERATURE IN TORONTO
FROM 1840 TO 1989

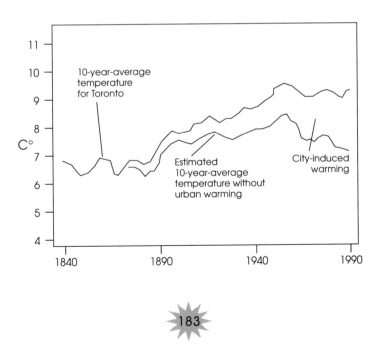

❄ In cities with a temperate climate, winds usually blow from the west, bringing fresh country air to the western side and transporting smoke and pollution to the eastern side. As a result, neighbourhoods on the western sides of mid-latitude cities are usually considered more fashionable.

150 years ago and in preserving the climate record over that period is exceedingly important today. These past observations are not just old weather. Although many people regard weather as simply an indication of how pleasant the day will be, or what outdoor conditions can be expected, weather data may be used to great advantage by many people, from insurers settling damage claims due to slips and slides, to farmers determining the risks posed by unseasonable freezes and droughts, and from homeowners locating the best spot for a skylight or windbreak, to those choosing retirement homes or havens from weather-related ailments. Moreover, high quality and long, continuous climate records from every province of Canada, some of them spanning over 100 years, constitute a useful data base for the study of global warming and climate change. In this context, weather information is more useful and more important than ever before.

An inspection of the annual temperatures for Toronto from 1840 to the present reveals considerable variation over the years. The coldest year was 1875, with an average temperature of 4.8°C. The warmest year, 1953, averaged 10.2°C, although 1987 was a close second at 10.1°C. By averaging these annual temperatures over 10-year periods, it is possible to smooth out the yearly swings and reveal a remarkable trend: as Toronto has grown, the average temperature also has increased. The 1980s were nearly 2.0°C warmer than 100 years ago, when Toronto's population was one-quarter its present size.

❄ The average relative humidity is 6 percent lower in cities than in the country, on an annual basis.

How much of this 20th-century warming is due to general climate change over southern Ontario and how much is due to the urbanization of Toronto? The extent to which warming can be attributed to natural causes (such as fluctuations in the earth's orbit around the sun, variations in the tilt of the earth's axis of rotation, changes in solar energy output, or drifting of the continents) or to human processes (burning of carbon dioxide and other greenhouse gases, deforestation and other massive land use changes) is still debatable. The increasing warmth of our cities ranks along with industrialization and deforestation worldwide as important reasons for the global warming of the atmosphere and recent climate change.

Large cities like Toronto can produce their own weather and local greenhouse effect. Compared with the surrounding countryside, cities have lighter winds (except around tall buildings), and humidity and visibility are lower. They also experience less sunshine, more cloud, fog, thunderstorms and rain, and less snow. But the most significant influence of urbanization is on temperature. Most large cities serve as gigantic radiators, warming up the outside air. Office buildings, factories, cars and people give off enormous quantities of heat. This is absorbed by brick, concrete and asphalt during the day, and radiated back into the air at night, preventing the city from cooling off. The "heat island" effect is most noticeable on clear, calm nights and early mornings in the winter, leaving the city 5°C to 8°C warmer than its environs. In summer, daytime temperatures are 1°C to 2°C higher in urban areas. Generally, the degree of warming increases with the size of the city and its population density. Temperatures are normally highest near the city core and decline gradually toward the

❄ Ultraviolet radiation in cities is 5 percent less in summer and as much as 30 percent less in winter compared to rural settings.

Office towers in downtown Toronto often create wind tunnels. TORONTO STAR SYNDICATE

suburbs, beyond which there is a steep temperature drop.

The variation of weather across Toronto can be significant. The weather at Pearson International Airport can be quite different from that at the corner of Bloor and Bay or in one of the surrounding suburbs. Even when averaged over a long period, climatic differences between the city core and the outskirts may be significant.

❄ Cities receive 10 percent more precipitation and have 10 percent more days of low ceilings and cloudiness than rural areas do.

Comparing Toronto's 100-year temperature record with that of a rural weather station illustrates the extent of Toronto's warming. The weather station at Parry Sound, Ontario (about 225 kilometres northwest of Toronto), is outside the town in hilly, partly wooded terrain. It has

186

a reliable 100-year temperature record, making it a good benchmark for comparing recent climate change in Southern Ontario. Parry Sound's warming is not as dramatic as Toronto's, being only about 0.4°C in 100 years. Nonetheless, it is comparable to the average rise in global temperature over the same period. On the other hand, Toronto is at least 2°C warmer now than 100 years ago. If the temperature rise at Parry Sound is attributed to climate change across southern Ontario, then the remainder of Toronto's warming, 1.6°C, could be attributed to urbanization.

❄ Fog is 30 percent and 100 percent more frequent in cities than in rural settings in summer and winter, respectively.

Cities in higher latitudes can reap several benefits from this added urban warmth, including lower heating bills. Heating costs for the same house would be about 15 percent higher in Richmond Hill, north of Toronto, than in the city centre. The extra warmth also means 15 to 30 percent fewer snow days in downtown Toronto, reducing the depth and duration of snow cover, lowering the cost of snow removal, and decreasing the number of traffic slowdowns. Another benefit of the urban heat island is a longer gardening season. Downtown Toronto averages 191 frost-free days per year. This drops off to 164 days in North York and to 145 days in towns farther north. The season for backyard gardening lasts as much as three to four weeks longer, and first killing frosts are often less severe in Toronto than in nearby communities, owing principally to the city's heat sources. Ornamental shrubs and plants that normally grow 300 kilometres farther south may be able to survive in Toronto, but not in the surrounding countryside.

Whether Toronto's microclimate will get even warmer over the next 150 years remains to be seen. But with each passing day, observers there and in other Canadian communities add another page to our weather history. From their records we will gain a greater understanding of our changing climate in the years ahead.

WEATHER —
MORE THAN
TOMORROW'S
FORECAST

CRIME-BUSTING CLIMATOLOGISTS

I F THE IDEA OF A WEATHERMAN WORKING ALONGSIDE crown attorneys, forensic scientists and fraud squads seems improbable, then meet David Murdoch, Canada's first and foremost crime-fighting climatologist. Short and heavy-set with the voice of a burly desk sergeant, Murdoch began his career as Canada's first crime-fighting weatherman when he started up the Ontario Forensic Climatology Unit for Environment Canada in 1973. Before that, he was an observer and weather briefer, first in his home town of Sudbury and later in Windsor, North Bay, Ottawa and Toronto.

In Murdoch's first case in 1976, which made judicial history in Canada, a Sudbury motorist was charged with running a stop sign and causing a serious accident. At this trial, the accused produced a photograph that he claimed had been taken immediately after the accident. It showed the stop sign lying in a ditch covered with mud. Testifying on behalf of the Crown, Murdoch produced his own photograph, a satellite picture showing clear skies over Sudbury except for the familiar smelter plumes. There was cloud cover in the defendant's photo. Confronted with this evidence, the motorist admitted he was lying and that he had taken his photo days after the accident. For the first time, a weather satellite image had been used as key evidence in a Canadian courtroom.

A veteran of 36 years in the weather business, Murdoch retired in 1990 from Environment Canada and is now a consultant. To date, he has testified 541 times in court; 93 of those cases were homicides, the others ranged from theft to bawdy-house charges.

Although Murdoch is the only full-time forensic climatologist in Canada, many other Environment Canada personnel receive subpoenas as expert witnesses, though few relish, as much as Murdoch, the prospect of preparing for a case, testifying under oath and facing gruelling cross-examination. He works hard to take into account what a judge told him many years ago: "A witness whose appearance is disorganized is disorganized." Says Murdoch, "This refers to more than how you dress or what you put into your briefcase. I want to know everything about the information I present. How long have weather observations been taken at a site? When were the instruments last inspected, and was the equipment working? Also important is the discipline to stay within one's bounds of expertise and to resist the temptation to speculate and embellish the facts."

Forensic weather investigations have nothing to do with future weather, only past events. Nevertheless, the tools that Murdoch and his former colleagues at Environment Canada use for solving murders; presenting evidence at inquests or hearings of discovery; determining the causes of slips and falls, industrial accidents or aircraft crashes; or assisting in unresolved insurance claims or contractual disputes are those of the weather forecaster — satellite images, radar printouts, weather charts and climatological records.

Lawyers and their clients are often amazed by the part that weather plays in criminal and civil cases. Air

> ❄ Lawyers for a farmer requested information from Environment Canada on the build up of hoar frost on hydro wires near Manitou, Manitoba, that resulted in a power interruption and the resultant loss of a flock of broiler chickens.

temperature and wind chill are vital clues in solving homicide cases, because they affect the rate a body cools and can help determine the time of death. Wind speed and direction may explain voices or gunshots heard downwind, or account for the movement of smoke or odors. Cloud cover, a full moon and restrictions to vision, such as fog and snow, help in the identification of suspects. The presence of dew or snow on the ground can explain wet shoes or footprints.

When called by judicial authorities, weather-detective employees of Environment Canada have at their fingertips weather maps, summaries and reports that can pin down at a glance what the weather was like on the day of the crime: when sunny periods occurred; how fast and from what direction the wind blew; whether rain or snow fell and for how long; whether lightning accompanied a storm; and how the temperature varied in the ground, at the surface and in the upper air. Complementing the climate sources are weather radar pictures and satellite photos to help fill in the gaps between weather recording stations. Preferring office time to court time, the meteorological staff gladly issue certified weather records or prepare plain-language explanations of weather circumstances in the hope that this written evidence will preclude a lengthy court appearance.

> ❄ The RCMP once asked Environment Canada whether the humidity was sufficiently high on a particular day to cause discomfort serious enough to trigger a murder.

Although the climate expert has not personally recorded the weather observations at the time in question, he or she is permitted under the Canada Evidence Act to present documentation that an observation was taken. It may be circumstantial evidence but is nonetheless admissible. In many investigations, the forensic climatologist is simply asked to establish the occurrence or non-occurrence of a weather phenomenon. In "The Case of the Rain-Delayed Mail," as I call it, a postman accused of taking letters home claimed he was just drying out rain-soaked mail. Expert testimony revealed that no rain had occurred along the mail route for several days before and after the postmarks on the letter.

In "The Case of Dew You Know the Way," three armed men accosted a beer store employee outside the store. When ordered back inside, the employee fled. One robber fired a shot at him but missed, the bullet striking one of his buddies in the abdomen. The other two took off across a field leaving the wounded man behind — and their footprints in the mud and dew-covered grass. Police followed the trail to the back of a garage where the two were apprehended. The weather people were asked to verify that atmospheric conditions were ideal for the formation of dew.

Weather is often ignored by those commiting a crime. In "The Case of the Misdirected Fire," a man tried to collect insurance for a fire that the insurance company claimed was deliberately set. The suspect said he had poured gasoline down the sparkplug holes of his stalled snowmobile in order to start it. The engine backfired, setting the machine on fire, and eventually the flames spread from the snowmobile shed to his cottage, he claimed. However, a climate expert testified the sparks would have had to travel 170 metres against a strong wind on a day with high humidity, and then set ablaze a cottage roof covered with snow. Not possible, ruled the court, and the man was found guilty of arson.

In another insurance fraud case, "Lightning Never Struck Once," a man with the help of a welder friend tried to fake a lightning strike during a heavy rainstorm. He had not been able to get replacement parts for an expensive refrigerator he had purchased a couple of years before and decided lightning damage would get him a new one. The two waited for a rainy night, backed up a portable welding machine to the house fuse box and zapped it. But they had overlooked one simple fact: no lightning during the storm. A climatologist testified in court that the radar scope, which can also detect lightning strokes, did not record one that night. The two confessed to the illegal act. As it turned out, a violent thunderstorm with continuous lightning crossed the region four days later!

Lightning was also not relevant in another case. The prosecution contended that the victim in a murder case had been having an affair and that his jealous wife had torched their cottage killing her husband. The defence argued that a lightning strike from a passing thunderstorm had ignited the building. No so, said the climatologist, who presented conclusive evidence that no thunderstorm activity had occurred in the area on the night in question.

Often, the climatologist is required to explain in lay terms to a judge or jury complicated weather processes that lie behind the evidence. "The Case of the Mysterious Fog Bank" concerned a fatal collision involving nine tractor trailers and several cars on a bridge over the Trent River near Trenton, Ontario. Nearby weather stations were reporting clear weather at the time. Murdoch explained that on that cold January night a patch of warm air above the open water drifted over the bridge. The first truck punched a hole through the air, creating swirls that mixed the warm and cold air masses and, suddenly, a wall of dense fog formed. As the vehicles in the lead slowed down, the following vehicles ploughed into them.

Some cases require careful documenting of weather events using a host of sources. In another tragic case, an Ontario Provincial Police officer who went to the aid of a woman in a stalled vehicle was killed by a tractor-trailer. The accident happened on the Garden City Skyway near St. Catharines in winter. The truck driver claimed a whiteout was to blame. The OPP contacted David Murdoch, who reconstructed a minute-by-minute account of the weather near St. Catharines prior to the accident using surface weather records, wind-recording charts from automatic stations, precipitation radar print-outs and satellite pictures. He even consulted his colleagues in Buffalo to confirm conditions minutes before the accident. In the thick dossier he handed to the crown attorney was a detailed analysis concluding that the snow had ended in the area more than two hours before the accident and that the visibility had been good. Winds might have produced some ground drifting on the road below the skyway, but this would not have affected visibility on the elevated road.

Solving some mysteries calls for creative guesswork. One autumn, forestry officials wanted to know why there were so many unexplained forest fires along the Trans-Canada Highway between Sudbury and Sault Ste. Marie. The weather people had no records of thunderstorms and lightning strikes during the outbreaks; conditions had been fine, sunny and warm. Faulty hotboxes on the Canadian Pacific Railway lines were also ruled out as a cause of the fires. "It was the beautiful fall colours causing the problem," says Murdoch. "Drivers would pull off the road to admire them. The heat from their car exhaust systems would scorch the tall grass. While the drivers were pulling away,

❄ The expert climatologist is allowed to present certified documents of weather observations, even though he or she has not taken or witnessed the weather observation. The Canada Evidence Act, Section 30, Subsection 1 states "Where oral evidence would be admissible, then in lieu of such information, a record made in the course of business or procedure is acceptable."

the wind would fan the fire and spread the flames. Being a Volkswagen owner, I knew that in early models the cata-lytic converters could heat up to 700°C and melt your driveway if you left the engine running long enough." The problem disappeared after the Ministry of Natural Resources constructed more viewing points along the highway the following spring.

At a coroner's inquest investigating the death of a young girl killed at a railway level crossing, suicide was suggested as the likely cause. However, Murdoch con-firmed the suspicions of a police officer that a cold, driving rain could have prompted the girl to raise her coat hood and turn away from the wind, muffling the sound of the oncoming train. The tragedy was ruled an accident.

For his suit in small claims court, an importer of Swiss chocolate bars needed certified weather data to prove neg-ligence by the cargo handlers. They unloaded his choco-late bars onto a loading dock in summer and left them unattended for a couple of days. The ensuing heat had turned the chocolate bars into chocolate pudding.

In "The Case of the Whores and Whorls," a morality officer, working between seven and 10 p.m., testified he could see inside a downtown bawdy-house because gusty winds kept blowing the curtains aside. The defence argued the night was cool and overcast with rain, but not windy. Murdoch's testimony confirmed both accounts. The night was warm in the early evening, but around 10 a distur-bance with gusty winds moved through the city followed by much cooler air and rain.

Whenever police are called in to investigate an inci-dent, forensic weather sleuths like David Murdoch can often find the meteorological "fingerprint" that helps solve the case.

DEAR CLIMATOLOGIST . . .

A N INVESTOR OF NEW FOOTWEAR FOR WALKING ON water was anxious to test its suitability under various weather conditions over Lake Ontario.

A woman in Lusket, Nova Scotia, wanted to know what the weather had been on February 16 in each of the past seven years to decide whether that date would be a good one for her wedding.

Officials from the Alberta Fish and Wildlife Department wondered whether the high incidence of chinooks one winter caused a massive die-off of antelope.

The Royal Air Force received Canadian climate data to determine when and where to test the effect of snow on helicopter operations.

Two inmates at Dorchester Penitentiary in New Brunswick, who were appealing a second-degree murder sentence, requested rainfall data, calling it crucial for their defence.

> ❄ A lawn sprinkler manufacturer wanted nationwide rainfall data to aid in its sales planning.

If there is one thing Canadians have in common, it is an insatiable appetite for information about the weather. One might think we get our fill from television, radio and newspapers, but a quick peek at a climatologist's mail suggests otherwise: Environment Canada weather offices are deluged with more than 200,000 requests for past weather records or climate information annually.

Some requests are amusing. One young student from Newfoundland with a fast-approaching deadline wrote, "Rush all the information you can get on our weather and weather all across the world, for free." An Alberta child wanted information on acid rain, "including a sample."

❄ A Swedish horticulture group requested Canadian climate data in order to determine which of Canada's shrubs and trees might survive in their climate conditions.

Requests can be bizarre. Take, for example, the Montreal man who requested information to confirm his suspicion that UFOs had flown over Montreal on the night of November 7, 1991. Meteorologist Jacques Miron recalls that the man wanted all available data, including satellite pictures, air-density readings and specific cloud conditions. He paid $150 for the information, which included an observation by a Quebec forecaster that cloud conditions created a luminous ring over Montreal that evening. Other unusual requests were:

• A housewife in Cranbrook wanted to know what weather conditions prevent mayonnaise from failing during its making.

• Someone was convinced that relative humidity correlated well with the winning numbers in a major lottery.

• A manufacturer of fibreglass portable toilets needed data on temperature extremes to calculate the likelihood of the chemical-water solution freezing.

Some inquiries are trivial, such as the one about a $100 bet riding on whether Hurricane Hazel was the same storm that caused the Red River flood. (They were four years apart.) However, most are serious questions concerning health or safety, economics and the environment.

Those requesting historical climate data range from farmers or gardeners worried about unusual conditions, to large oil companies concerned with the impact of climate extremes on drilling platforms and tankers. Users can be found in every sector of society, and applications are in nearly everything climatologists do. Requests come from entrepreneurs starting a business, from industry representatives worried about the weathering of stockpiled material, from individuals planning a dream vacation, from researchers, from government officials, indeed, from all for whom the future weather is important.

Physicians, health workers and medical researchers frequently ask for weather information to treat those suffering from asthma, hay fever and migraines. The Institute for the Achievement of Human Potential in Pennsylvania wrote for weather data needed to discover weather conditions causing children's seizures. In October 1991, the Toronto Children's Aid Society asked about the weather occurring on a particular day in Halifax seven years ago. The dossier on one of their recently arrived wards was so thin that any information about the weather on the day the child was born would give them some place to start.

Thousands of health-related requests are received annually from individuals. "I am 68 years old, have heart disease and rheumatism and suffer migraine attacks," one person wrote. "Please, where can I relocate to find clean air, a mild climate and generally a more healthy place to live." A father wrote seeking some place in Canada with dry conditions similar to those in Israel where his son's asthma had improved during a summer visit.

❄ An automobile company requested information on the coldest, windiest, wettest site in Canada to test performance of a foreign compact car in winter driving conditions.

Environment Canada has a wide range of resources to help Canadians answer their climatological queries. Six climatologists at regional weather offices have a vast array of publications, computer archives, log sheets, record charts and satellite pictures at their fingertips. In addition, Environment Canada's large facility in Downsview, Ontario, contains records ranging from handwritten 19th-century weather ledgers to sophisticated satellite and radar imagery. Its archives are accumulating observations at more than 40 million a year from a far-flung Canadian network of land, upper-air and over-water stations. Its total archive is estimated to contain more than three billion observations from some 8,600 Canadian locations.

Weather records also have legal applications. Most requests are from lawyers involved in civil suits. Often these involve insurance cases from settling property damage claims to verifying slips and falls. In a Toronto incident, a thunderstorm knocked out power at a fish store, and the ensuing smell of rotting fish forced tenants above the store to evacuate. The insurance company refused the claim because no thunderstorm was reported at Pearson International Airport that evening. When the owner of the building contacted climatologist Bryan Smith, he confirmed that a thunderstorm had occurred at Toronto Island Airport, which is closer to the fish store, and the insurance company agreed to pay damages.

In another civil suit, the Minnesota North Stars took legal action against the Quebec Nordiques in 1980. Minnesota sued Quebec for $64,000 for failing to show up for a hockey game. In their successful defence, the Nordiques' lawyers subpoenaed climatologist Gérard Chapleau, who testified that thick fog prevented the team's plane from taking off.

From balloonists to boaters, outdoor enthusiasts recognize the value of historical weather in planning future activities. Ski operators from Marble Mountain, Newfoundland, to Whistler, British Columbia, have written to obtain snowfall data, or the frequency of weather suitable for snowmaking. One call from a Mexican consulate requested information on summer-snow skiing and skating opportunities at Blue Mountain Lodge and Horseshoe Valley in southern Ontario. The president of a large United

> ❄ Mexican tourists phoned looking for summer snow skiing in southern Ontario.

States corporation inquired about the weather he could expect for a planned two-month canoe trip down the Churchill River. The big game committee of the Ontario Federation of Anglers and Hunters requested climate information to support their proposal for an earlier moose season. Marathon swimmer Jocelyn Muir asked for average wind speed and direction to help plan a possible summer swim along the ferry routes to and from Prince Edward Island.

> ❄ A manufacturer of fibreglass portable toilets needed data on temperature extremes to calculate the likelihood of the chemical-water solution freezing.

The research community is a major end user of climate-related data. One Ph.D. student studied tree rings from black spruce in Kouchibouguac National Park in New Brunswick to detect climatic fluctuations. Another graduate student from Wyoming wanted Canadian weather data for his research on how weather influences the body size of North American mammals.

The application for climate information in business and industry ranges from locating, designing and operating thermal or nuclear plants to managing seasonal changes in glues for piano manufacturing. Weather statistics have been used to explain fluctuations in beer sales, develop a new series of chemical de-icers, and schedule advertising campaigns for seasonal products. One request for low-temperature and wind-speed data was useful in selecting metal for ship hulls in the Arctic. The same data were useful in assessing the vulnerability of caribou calves to spring storms.

Architects and builders now routinely use snow- and ice-load values or the probability of severe-weather events to design structures capable of withstanding climate stresses. House builders interested in the feasibility of harnessing wind currents to pump water, and solar energy to heat the water, would be wise to obtain past climate data.

An Ontario Provincial Police officer stands on duty in a flooded Cambridge, Ontario street. PHOTO, THE HAMILTON SPECTATOR

Home-owners can also use climate data for such purposes as planning the best location for a windbreak or a new skylight.

Some of the most interesting requests come from authors seeking to add realism to an adventure story or to examine the significance of weather in historic events. Canadian author Scott Young sought March sunrise and sunset times at Spence Bay, Northwest Territories, to help develop the story line for his mystery novel, *The Shaman's Knife*. A professor from Columbia University wanted to determine barometric pressure changes caused by the shock wave resulting from the Halifax explosion of December 6, 1917. One researcher's request may

❄ One person called convinced that relative humidity correlated well with the winning numbers in a major lottery.

lead to a whole new category for baseball statisticians: he asked for Toronto and Montreal barometric data, hoping to correlate air-pressure conditions and the effectiveness of certain relief pitchers.

The breadth and scope of the applications of historical weather data are almost limitless. From planning outdoor wedding ceremonies to ideal mating conditions for queen bees, if your question is about past weather, the climatologist probably has the answer.

THE SNEEZING SEASON

WHEN MOST CANADIANS ARE ENJOYING THE BEAUTY and delights of summer, at least four million of us are enduring bouts of sneezing, wheezing and itching during the annual hay fever season. Sufferers are easily spotted by their red, baggy eyes, stuffy or drippy nose, and prolonged sneezing spells. Some also have asthma attacks. There is much personal misery and a high loss of productivity.

> ❄ An average sneeze produces a tornado-force wind of 200 kilometres per hour.

The term *hay fever*, a popular misnomer for allergic rhinitis, was coined in the 19th century by English doctors to describe the feverish bouts of sneezing and snuffling that people commonly suffer around haying time. Yet hay is not the only cause and fever is seldom a symptom. Instead, hay fever is triggered by tiny, airborne allergens, such as mould spores or pollen from trees, shrubs, grasses and weeds.

What is it about pollen that causes allergic reactions? Pollen grains carry 30 to 40 different proteins. When the pollen is inhaled, the proteins are released. For some people, and for reasons that are still not known, the

❄ Adolescence is the peak time for the onset of hayfever; it rarely emerges in old age. Hayfever can persist for a lifetime or vanish after a year or two; stay vanished or re-emerge years later.

immune system produces a special class of antibodies in an attempt to rid the body of the pollen. These antibodies seek out two types of specialized cells, mast cells and basophils, and attach themselves to their surfaces. When the pollen proteins come in contact with these cells during subsequent exposures, they bind with the antibodies, causing the cells to burst open. This reaction releases many chemicals, the most important one being histamine, which causes the surrounding tissues to swell and leak more mucus, producing the familiar symptoms of hay fever.

Pollen is present in the air year-round but the concentration is highest during the growing season, from March to the killing frost in October. People who are allergic to more than one species of plant may experience a protracted hay fever season because the flowering periods of individual species overlap.

Trees and shrubs pollinate first, generally from mid-April to late May, but earlier in British Columbia. Grasses come next, pollinating from late May to late July. Ironically, the varieties of grass that cause the most reactions, such as timothy and Kentucky bluegrass, are the ones we try the hardest to cultivate in our lawns. Herbs and weeds, which are the worst offenders, pollinate in late summer. The worst of them is common ragweed (*Ambrosia artemisiifolia*). Of all the seasonal allergens, it produces the most irritating pollen, followed closely by birch trees. Nearly 90 percent of all people who suffer from hay fever are allergic to ragweed. Incredibly, a single plant produces a billion grains of pollen, yet three or four grains may be all that it takes to cause the symptoms of hay fever.

Many allergenic weeds thrive on vacant lots and along

fence rows and roadside ditches. Very few are found in virgin forests, swamps or mountains. In cities, pollen counts tend to be lower downtown and higher near the outskirts. Agriculture Canada's map of ragweed pollen density across Canada shows, in general, that the agricultural lands of southern Ontario and Quebec are infested with ragweed. Apart from the extreme southern portions of Manitoba, Saskatchewan and Alberta, the Prairies are mainly free of ragweed, as are British Columbia, Northern Ontario and most of Atlantic Canada. Infestations of giant ragweed in Manitoba's rich agricultural south make it a bane for hay fever sufferers. Christine Rogers, a botanist doing research at the University of Toronto, says the Toronto region has one of the longest and more severe allergenic pollen seasons of any major urban centre in North America because it is at the centre of common ragweed's range, and birch trees are also prevalent.

> ❄ Pollen counts vary widely from day to day and from season to season. An extremely high reading of 250 pollen grains per cubic metre of air can be followed the next day with a reading of only 25.

Although many hay fever sufferers are quick to blame ragweed pollen, they may be just as allergic to moulds. These peak in summer and fall during grass-cutting and leaf-raking times. Only if a snow cover exists or the ground is frozen do mould counts decline. They tend to be highest on humid and windy days, which promote their growth and dispersal. Mould spores and pollen grains ride the prevailing winds from the south, where flowering plants flourish year-round. Cool nighttime air often contains more mould than daytime air.

Hay fever sufferers know only too well that their misery can vary greatly from day to day and year to year. Symptoms can be brought on by just about everything from exercise to air pollution, but weather is the main controlling factor.

Temperature, humidity, rain and wind have a considerable impact on the duration and severity of the hay fever season. They also affect the timing of the release of pollen, its concentration, and its distribution.

At higher latitudes, flowering commences later than in the south and frosts come earlier, resulting in a generally shorter pollen-producing season. Wet, warm spring weather stimulates vegetation growth and flowering, but a heavy rainfall will wash the air clean of pollen grains. Although temperature is also critical, it is usually the climate of the previous season that influences total pollen production. In the previous summer, many tree species form their flower buds for the following year. Once set, only a late spring frost or very wet weather can decrease the overall pollen yield.

Daily weather affects the release of pollen at a given location in several ways. Clear, hot, sunny and windy days frequently send pollen counts soaring, while cool, humid and rainy days often bring relief. The greatest amount of pollen is released in the morning between eight o'clock and noon, when the humidity drops with solar warming. The anthers of plants dry and burst open at this time. Heavy dew or early morning showers will ground much of the pollen or delay its takeoff, decreasing the supply available for that day's transport. Afternoon rains also reduce the supply.

Dry, sunny and windy weather favours dispersal. Light winds and strong convection carry much of the fresh pollen and mould spores into the higher, speedier airstreams, often spreading it over a few kilometres, and sometimes as far as 700 kilometres. Pollen grains that have settled to the ground may be refloated by local air turbulence associated with thunderstorms or cold

> ❄ Each fall more than 250 million tonnes of ragweed pollen are blown across Ontario and Quebec.

206

fronts. Wind direction is also important. If the wind blows from an upwind, heavily ragweed-infested area during flowering, high pollen counts are likely to occur downwind. If the wind trajectory brings the air mass from the sea or other non-flowering areas, lower pollen concentrations would be expected. Obviously, knowledge of weather forecasts can be a great help to someone trying to avoid or minimize the effect of hay fever episodes.

❄ The average person circulates about 12 cubic metres of air through the lungs daily. This means a staggering 1,000 billion solid air particles per day pass through the respiratory system of the average urban dweller.

The first line of defence against allergens is avoidance. Although it may be impossible to escape airborne pollen totally, it is possible to reduce exposure and the severity of the reaction by keeping windows closed and curtailing morning activities outside. The particular plants one is allergic to can be identified through skin testing and correlation with the time of year the symptoms occur. It's a good idea to learn to identify these plants, get to know when they flower and then to stay at least 100 metres away if possible. For some patients, allergy shots and antihistamines are effective in reducing the symptoms of hay fever. There are also prescription medications available for those with severe symptoms.

In extreme cases, sufferers from hay fever may decide to move to another climate free from the particular allergen. However, a change of scenery does not always bring a breath of fresh air. Grass pollen is so prevalent it is difficult to avoid, except on an ocean voyage or by moving to a polar climate. Because there are many factors that cause hay fever, the Allergy Information Association suggests a change of climate should be considered only as a last resort after other appropriate methods of controlling the symptoms have been tried. Of course, in every case, proper medical care should be sought.

TIME TO TAP THE SAP

A H, THOSE FIRST SIGNS OF SPRING — MILLIONAIRE baseball players warming up in the Florida sun, crocuses sprouting, meltwater rushing into streams and rivers; and a visit to the local sugar bush to taste the new crop of maple syrup.

Almost the entire world production of maple syrup and sugar comes from a band of hardwood maple forests stretching from Ontario to Nova Scotia and south into adjacent states. Canada produces about 70 percent of this, with two-thirds of world production by volume coming from Quebec alone.

Sugaring off, a time-honoured spring tradition in Eastern Canada, dates from before 1600. Native North Americans were the first to collect maple sap to produce sugar. They also used the "sweet water" to give cooked venison a maple-cured flavour. Eventually, they shared their knowledge of tapping trees and evaporating sap with European settlers. Back then, maple sugar was a staple food and highly prized because it was the only readily available and cheap sweetener.

Several varieties of maple trees are tapped in Canada, including sugar, black, red and silver maples. However, the rock, or sugar, maple (*Acer saccharum*) is the only one tapped commercially, because it is a high-yielding sap producer and its sap is sweeter and more palatable than sap from other maples. The total value of Canadian maple products is less than $100 million. This is not a huge sum, but it represents an important source of income for some 10,000 small family-owned operations. For most commercial producers, tapping the sugar bush is a part-time business in areas where cash crops are not normally grown.

208

The success of the spring sap run largely depends on the weather. The making of a good maple season begins the previous year with a warm, sunny summer and ample moisture to promote a full, large crown of leaves and plentiful reserves of stored sap. A deep snow cover is crucial in winter to insulate tree roots in shallow soils where roots are close to the surface and in early spring to ensure adequate soil moisture. A cold winter without the presence of a deep snow cover will freeze the roots, likely leading to mortality. Roots must begin to thaw before the sap flows. A late fall or midwinter thaw followed by extreme cold can reduce sap yields and damage roots due to deep soil freezing or heaving.

❄ A product may be represented as pure maple syrup only if it is obtained exclusively from maple sap. If it is not a pure maple product, a complete list of ingredients in descending order of their proportions is required on the label.

But it's the spring weather that is the key to whether a bumper harvest of maple syrup can be expected. Long ago, producers recognized that once the trees begin to thaw, cold, frosty nights alternating with mild, sunny days trigger the start of the sap. Once the sap is flowing, these diurnal temperature swings also control its daily uptake and exudation. The best sap runs occur when the maximum daytime temperatures exceed 4°C following nights with temperatures below –4°C.

The rate of warming is also important. Too mild too soon often means sap becomes sour. Just as bad is the year's flow to take place all within a few days, causing a glut of unprocessed sap in the sugar shack, where bacteria can quickly reduce its quality.

Sap will deteriorate rapidly if there are no overnight freezes, and runs cease altogether when leaves begin to appear on the trees. When temperatures stay consistently above freezing, microorganisms — primarily yeasts and moulds — grow rapidly in the sap. The result is a darker syrup with a harsh, burnt flavour, which is considered to be of lower quality. In 1983, the sap run in southern Quebec stopped about a week after it started when afternoon temperatures of 15°C turned the sap bitter and cloudy.

Rain and snow during the sap run also seems to influence the harvest. An old weather adage says, If the maple sap runs faster, it is going to rain. Many producers believe this, saying that the sap flow is greater on wet days and on days preceding rain and snow. This is probably due to the lower atmospheric pressure associated with wet weather. Wet snow that sticks to twigs and branches also seems to stimulate good flows.

One of science's long-standing and most intriguing mysteries is how sap flows inside the sugar maple. For many years, root pressures and the lifting power of transpiring leaves were seen as the principal mechanisms for passing sap up the trunk and out the tap hole. However, stripped and severed trees and branches, where no transpiration whatever could occur, exude sap freely whenever the weather conditions are suitable.

Another explanation of why sap is sucked up during freezing and pushed out during thawing is the contraction and expansion of air. Although this process has been observed in other species, it's not the case with the flow of sap in maple trees. Apparently what happens is that on very cold nights the tree freezes from the outside into the stem. As the tree freezes, the warmer inner sap water is drawn towards the colder parts of the tree, adding to the ice crystals growing inside the wood cells. Tension is set up, and sap water is pulled up from the roots and trunk through the portions of the sapwood (xylem) not yet frozen. Subsequently, when the temperature rises sufficiently above freezing to

❄ Once the sap begins to flow in the sapwood, the sap is 97.5 percent water, 2.4 percent sugar and 0.1 percent minerals.

warm the trunk, sap in the ice crystals of the wood cells melts and further contributes to the movement of sap. The warmer the temperature, the greater the flow, but only to a point. If several nights pass without subzero temperatures, the flow will decrease.

❄ Once collected from the trees, the sap is boiled to a minimum concentration of 66 percent sugar. It takes roughly 30 to 40 litres of maple sap to make 1 litre of maple syrup.

For sap to flow out a tap hole, pressure inside the tree must be equal to or greater than the air pressure outside the tree. The speed at which freezing occurs affects the rate of ice crystal formation and the concentration of gases within the wood cells. On freezing, frost begins to form inside the gas-filled spaces of the wood fibre cells, much like frost forms on the inside of windows on a cold night. As the temperature rises, respiratory activity in the cells produces carbon dioxide. At higher temperatures, less gas is dissolved in solution. (It turns out that carbon dioxide is only half as soluble in water at 20°C as at 0°C.) Excess gas trapped in the wood increases pressure, and as the sap melts, it is pushed out the tap hole by the compressed gas. When the temperature drops, more of the carbon dioxide is absorbed in the sap water, the gas contracts, the pressure drops below that outside the tree, and the sap flow slows and eventually ceases for the night.

Although it is difficult to predict when the sap run will begin, maple syrup producers usually drill tap holes during the last week of February or the first week of March. Then they hope for at least six weeks of alternating warm days and cool nights. But weather variations from year to year are one of the major uncertainties maple producers face. Some poor sap runs in recent years have been blamed on thaws coming too early or too late. It is almost as if springs have been eliminated — a freezing March giving way to a sweltering April. The exception was 1992, when Canadian syrup production reaching 18.7 million litres. In the Eastern Townships of Quebec, the world's maple syrup capital, the warm weather did not arrive until April 20 and the sap run continued for almost nine weeks.

But such ideal conditions have been rare in the Eastern Townships. Weather statistics reveal, if not the absence of spring, at least a shorter transition season in many years with less ideal weather for sugaring off. Unlike the early 1970s, the 1980s' snow cover disappeared about a month earlier, temperatures rose above 15°C sooner, the sap run averaged about six weeks instead of eight, and there was a 25-percent decline in days with ideal freeze-thaw sequences.

❄ In the late 1980s, the number of commercial maple syrup producers totalled 8,000 in Quebec; 1,000 in Ontario; 44 in New Brunswick; and 100 in Nova Scotia.

Apart from weather variations, over the past two decades many producers have also been concerned about the overall health of sugar maples. Trees are growing only one-third as quickly today as they did 30 to 40 years ago, and maples that should live two or three centuries are losing their foliage at the relatively young age of 75. In the most-affected areas, maples in July look like the trees of November.

Many large sugar-bush operators and some scientists blame massive amounts of air pollution, including acid rain and low-level ozone, for the decline of maple trees. Highly acidic rain washes away soil and nutrients and frees toxic metals such as aluminum, which can destroy fine root hairs and block the uptake of important nutrients. Air pollution also weakens trees by defoliation, robbing them of their potential to photosynthesize, the process by which plants produce nourishment in the presence of sunlight. In south-western Quebec, the mountain woodlots are often shrouded in clouds containing acidic sulphates and nitrates, which also contribute to defoliation.

But other scientists and maple syrup producers say that no one has ever proven a tree has been killed by acid rain or acid mist. They argue that the once-invincible maple has many natural and human enemies. Tent caterpillars, diseases, forest mismanagement and climate change may all contribute to early mortality.

A 1992 report from Forestry Canada and the United States Forest Service suggests that acid rain may not be the problem. The joint study, initiated in 1988 after sugar maple stands started to die back in the early 1980s, says the leafy canopy at the top of trees appeared denser in areas of high acid rain. The preliminary report suggests that the poor health of maples was likely the result of biological and environmental factors, and especially adverse climate change.

Another 1992 report from the Ontario Ministry of the Environment concludes that maple trees have fallen prey to the strangely variable and extreme climate over the past 20 years. In particular, the number of short-term climate stresses has dramatically increased. Events such as droughts, early winter thaw followed by a deep freeze, poor snow cover combined with a hard freeze, and an abnormally warm or cold growing season combined with insects and disease have incited the decline of sugar maple in certain regions.

More research is needed to determine the long-term effect of climate and pollution on maple sugar trees, and it may be years before the full impact is clear. In the meantime, maple syrup producers hope for a bumper crop each spring, as do syrup lovers around the world who savor its sweetness on their morning pancakes.

> ❄ In 1900, the production of maple products in Canada totalled 10,001,400 litres. There were an estimated 55,000 producers working 23 million tap holes.

WEATHERPROOFING SPECTATOR EVENTS

OR MOST OUTDOOR BALL GAMES, FIELD CONDITIONS
and weather forecasts used to be as important as a
club's starting line-up, game plan and injury reserve
list. They were, at least, until the arrival of the dome, the
covered stadium phenomenon that in 25 years has swept
much — but not all — of the weather uncertainty out of
professional baseball and football games.

Twenty-two cities in Canada and the United States
have taken a cue from Houston, where the first covered
stadium originated in 1964, and roofed over their big-
league sports events. Two stadiums, the SkyDome in
Toronto and the Olympic Stadium in Montreal, have
gone a step further with the installation of retractable
roofs — ironically bringing an element of weather uncertainty back into sports events in the process.

In theory, a covered stadium is supposed to weatherproof an event. However, on June 15, 1976, a baseball
game at the Houston Astrodome was actually rained out.
The players were ready but the umpires, most of the staff
and the fans could not arrive due to a deluge of 250 millimetres of rain that flooded the streets and grounds
around the ballpark. At the Pontiac Silverdome, outside
Detroit, a March snowstorm in 1985 brought down its
fibreglass roof. In Minneapolis, heavy snow has caused the
Metrodome roof to collapse three times. Even the
SkyDome's retractable roof could not prevent a rain, or
roof, delay of six minutes during a baseball game in June
1989. Almost comically, the pitcher, catcher and umpire
ran for cover while the fielders stood watching and

214

waiting as sections of the dome rolled together above home plate.

Just as embarrassing were the two rain delays in less than two weeks at the Olympic Stadium in July 1989. One of the surprise showers was accompanied by high winds, which resulted in a two-hour wait before officials would lower the 65-tonne synthetic roof. The other delay lasted for almost an hour.

With strong winds, heavy snows and thick ice the norm at the SkyDome site, it was crucial that sophisticated microclimate studies be carried out. Miniature sky-domes were tested in a wind tunnel and a water flume under every conceivable wind force and snow load likely for the Toronto area. Wind speeds and directions were measured at 238 points on the roof. Crushed walnut shells were used to see how snow would blow, drift and settle on the roof. Snow buildup, rapid melting, heavy rains and the ensuing cascade of snow off the roof were simulated to estimate the maximum stress levels, especially at the end of the roof.

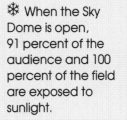

❄ When the Sky Dome is open, 91 percent of the audience and 100 percent of the field are exposed to sunlight.

The tests, which resulted in modifications to the roof's design, indicated that the dome could withstand the force of a hurricane. It is strong enough to open or close in winds gusting up to 64 kilometres per hour and can sustain snowdrifts up to five metres deep. (Toronto's deepest snow cover in 32 years of record keeping is 43 centimetres.) When open, the roof allows the sun to shine over the entire playing field and on 91 percent of the seats.

Understandably, few studies could be made of the weather inside the dome before its completion. Wind-tunnel tests had indicated that winds would be minimal at field level with the roof open, but actual playing conditions have brought a few surprises. Baseballs don't travel well in the teeth of turbulent winds at the roof opening, while moderate winds corkscrew down from the shelf over the north end and swirl back in toward the playing field.

To close or not to close is the big question being asked at the SkyDome and at Montreal's "Big O" (Olympic Stadium) these days. The final choice is that of the clubs in consultation with stadium managers, although the preference is for the roof to be closed, despite the baseball clubs' predilection for the outdoors where the game was meant to be played.

Stadium officials in Toronto and Montreal comply with club wishes whenever possible, but there are certain rules: roofs are sealed shut from the beginning of October to the beginning of May for winterizing; roofs are not moved during strong winds (those blowing greater than 25 kilometres per hour in Montreal and 65 kilometres per hour in Toronto); and if the roof is closed at the beginning of an event, it will stay closed, no matter how much the weather improves.

On some days, an early decision to open or close is possible. With warm temperatures, light winds and zero chance of rain, the roof is open; with unseasonably cool temperatures, scattered showers or strong gusty winds, it is closed. On other days the decision is not so easy. When there is a chance of rain, strong winds or other kinds of adverse weather, the forecast is studied and the weather watched with the help of a consulting meteorologist retained by stadium officials. The meteorologist monitors weather systems on the radar screen and is only a phone call away from the operator who pushes the close button. Both roofs can enclose their respective stadiums in 20 to 30 minutes, following some preparatory work.

❄ It takes about 750 horsepower — the equivalent power of six four-cylinder cars — to fully open the Skydome's retractable roof (the roof weighs 11,000 tonnes).

Would 35°C temperatures close the roof? Could it ever be too cool in the summer to close the roof? Would open-roof weather in May constitute the same in July with identical conditions? Stadium officials in Toronto and Montreal could not say whether they would open or shut the roof in certain weather situations. Both agree that it is a learning experience.

At a Toronto Blue Jays baseball game on June 10, 1989, the sky at the time of the first pitch was overcast, with a temperature of 15°C and moderate west winds. The roof was open but should have been closed. Fans dressed in summer shorts and sleeveless shirts shivered in their seats. Winds inside the dome swirled, garbage blew across the field, and long fly balls suddenly stopped and dropped. The same weather in April might have been ideal for fans wearing jackets or sweaters. Howard Starkman, Blue Jays publicity director, says the team is making up policy as it goes along. "It will take years of weather experience to develop open or shut criteria." Right now, there are no procedure books or decision strategies for opening or closing.

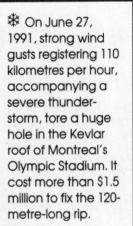

❄ On June 27, 1991, strong wind gusts registering 110 kilometres per hour, accompanying a severe thunderstorm, tore a huge hole in the Kevlar roof of Montreal's Olympic Stadium. It cost more than $1.5 million to fix the 120-metre-long rip.

What are the chances of going to the SkyDome or Olympic Stadium and watching an event with the roof open? To answer that question, one must attempt to define weather conditions suitable for viewing an outdoor attraction in comfort.

Open-roof weather in June, July and August might be defined as a full five-hour period with visibility greater than one kilometre, moderate winds less than 25 kilometres per hour, no rain, snow or thunder, and temperatures greater than 16°C in the afternoon or 14°C in the

❄ The first facility with a movable top was the National Tennis Centre in Melbourne, Australia, which opened in January, 1988. The tennis complex, home of the Australian Open, took less than two years to build at a cost of $79 million. The two retractable sections of the Melbourne roof weigh 320 tonnes each. The biggest roof panel at the Sky Dome weighs 1,906 tonnes.

evening. Except for temperature, dome weather criteria are the same in all months. Recognizing that spectators would wear sweaters and jackets in spring and fall, and heavy coats in winter, open-roof temperatures might exceed 14°C in May and September (12°C at night), 11°C in April and October (10°C at night), and 9°C during the cold season from November to March.

The accompanying table gives the chances of experiencing open-dome weather for Toronto, Montreal, Edmonton (there is talk of building a roof over Commonwealth Stadium), and Vancouver. Percentages are based on 36 years of weather data. It is clear that domes were meant for Canada. During 36 winters at the four cities, there were only 13 days in total when the dome could have been opened, based on the above criteria. However, in July and August, Toronto, Montreal and Vancouver have the same chance of open-dome weather; about three-quarters of the days. As a matter for study, stadium officials in Toronto and Montreal might consider delaying winterizing until after October 15 and advancing reopening to any time after the middle of April. This could extend the open-dome viewing season, weather permitting, by up to a month.

In the evening, there is 10 to 25 percent less chance of open-dome weather occurring from spring to early fall, mainly because temperature criteria fail to stay above the predefined limiting threshold for all five hours of an event. Rainfall doesn't make a significant difference, being on

CHANCES (PERCENT) OF OPEN-DOME WEATHER FOR AN AFTERNOON EVENT

	Jan.	Feb.	Mar.	Apr.	May	Jun.	Jul.	Aug.	Sept.	Oct.	Nov.	Dec.
Toronto	0	0	3	21	36	61	77	75	54	34	8	1
Montreal	0	0	2	21	40	60	73	69	48	29	5	0
Edmonton	0	0	2	21	34	44	63	56	34	24	1	0
Vancouver	0	0	0	21	40	44	76	76	45	34	0	0

average only one to two percent more frequent in the evening than in the afternoon. In Toronto, Montreal and Vancouver there is a better than even chance of having open-dome weather on summer evenings.

Baseball fans in Toronto and Montreal will never again suffer cold and wet. Some purists may miss the nasty weather factor, but come October, the World Series in Toronto or Montreal is fully weatherproof — no snow delays or frozen-out games in the North!

SELECT BIBLIOGRAPHY

Agriculture Canada. *Canadian Havens from Hay Fever.* Publication 1570, 1976.

Akasofu, Syun-Ichi. "The Dynamic Aurora." *Scientific American,* May 1989, 90-97.

Brown, Bruce. "Shedding Light on the Aurora." *National Wildlife,* February 1985, 51-53.

Brownlee, Shannon. "Forecasting: How Exact Is It?" *Discover,* April 1985, 10-29.

Callaghan, Morley. *Winter.* Toronto: McClelland and Stewart, 1974.

Campbell, Marjorie F. "The Day Niagara Stood Still." *Canadian Geographic,* January 1960, 28-33.

Canby, Thomas Y. "El Niño's Ill Wind." *National Geographic,* February 1984, 144-183.

Christison, Tim. "Snow-eater." *Nature Canada,* Spring 1985.

Collins, Richard L. "Understanding the Jet Stream." *Flying,* November 1983, 53.

Coons, C.F. *Sugar Bush Management for Maple Syrup Producers.* Ontario Ministry of Natural Resources, 1987.

Court, Arnold. "Wind Chill." *The Bulletin of the American Meteorological Society,* December 1948, 487-493.

Daglish, Susan. *Avoiding Airborne Allergens.* Allergy Information Association, 1981.

Douglas, Paul. *Prairie Skies.* Stillwater, MS: Voyageur Press, 1990.

Driscoll, Dennis M. "Windchill: The 'Brrr' Index." *Weatherwise,* December 1987, 321-326.

Forrester, Frank H. "Winds of the World." *Weatherwise,* October 1982, 204-210.

Fraser, Alistar B. "Chasing Rainbows." *Weatherwise,* December 1983, 280-288.

Freier, George D. *Weather Proverbs.* Tucson, AZ: Fisher Books, 1992.

Gauthier, Monique. "Indian Summer." *Chinook,* Winter 1986, 7-9.

Gilbert, Bill. "A Groundhog's 'Day' Means More to Us Than It Does to Him." *Smithsonian,* February 1985, 60-69.

Greenler, Robert. *Rainbows, Halos and Glories.* New York: Cambridge University Press, 1980.

Holford, Ingrid. *The Guinness Book of Weather Facts and Feats.* Enfield, Middlesex: Guinness Superlatives Ltd., 1977.

Hornstein, Reuben A. *The Weather Book.* Toronto: McClelland and Stewart, 1980.

Khandekar, Madhav L. "What? El Niño? Where?" *Climatic Perspectives*, Environment Canada, February 1992, 9-13.

Kim, Y.T., and R.H. Leech. "Effects of Climatic Conditions on Sap Flow in Sugar Maple." *Forestry Chronicle*, August 1985, 303-307.

Landsberg, H.E. "Climates and Urban Planning." In *Urban Climates*, Technical Note 108, World Meteorological Organization, 1970.

Lockhart, Gary. *The Weather Companion*. New York: Wiley Science Editions, 1988.

Logan, Ron. "The January Thaw." *Weatherwise*, December 1982, 263-267.

McLaughlin, D.L. *Etiology of Sugar Maple Decline at Selected Sites in Ontario*. Ontario Ministry of the Environment, 1992.

McMorine, J.G.S., and G.A. McKay. *Storm Rainfall and Runoff at Buffalo Gap, Saskatchewan*. Regina: Prairie Farm Rehabilitation Administration, July 1962.

Payne, Doug. "Environmental Eye." *New Scientist*, August 5, 1982.

Phillips, David. *The Climates of Canada*. Supply and Services Canada, 1990.

Potemra, Thomas A. "Aurora Borealis: The Greatest Light Show on Earth." *Smithsonian*, February 1977, 64-71.

Reimer, Phil. *Phil Reimer's B.C. Weather Book*. Vancouver: Phil Reimer Communications, 1991.

Shabbar, Amir. *AES Monthly Forecast Techniques and Verification*. Canadian Climate Centre Report No. 91-3, 1991.

Smith, Bryan. "Climatology Goes to Court." *Climatological Bulletin*, 1988.

Somerville, Scott. "Heat and Drought, 1930's Style." *Chinook*, Autumn 1981, 10-11.

Stolarski, Richard S. "The Antarctic Ozone Hole." *Scientific American*, January 1988, 30-36.

Thomas, Morley. "−81°F. The Canadian Record Low." *Weatherwise*, December 1963, 270-271.

Tyree, Melvin T. "Maple Sap Uptake." *Plant Physiology*, 1983, 277-285.

Wyatt, Valerie. *Weather Watch*. Toronto: Kids Can Press, 1990.

INDEX